MY LIFE & MY VIEWS

MAX BORN

My Life & My Views

Introduction by

I. BERNARD COHEN

Professor of the History of Science
Harvard University

Charles Scribner's Sons, New York

Contents

MY LIFE & MY VIEWS

Introduction

Max Born commands a special kind of esteem in scientific circles as a physicist's physicist—especially for those of my generation who learned their physics during the thirties and forties. In part, his reputation among us was a natural consequence of his authorship of the basic introductory textbook on atomic physics for science students, which during some seven editions introduced budding physicists and chemists to this then-recondite subject. On a higher level, he was also the author of a modern treatise on crystals and a magnificent adult presentation of optics.

For scientists, furthermore, Born achieved a commanding position for the distinguishing qualities of his interpretation of the quantum mechanics he helped to create: a truly physical interpretation, based on the concepts of probability, in place of the more generally accepted abstract formalism. His position led him clearly to a rather astonishing generalization, that there can be no simple determinism on the atomic scale of events. In the essays and lectures composing the present volume (which were written between 1955 and 1965 and have been edited for book publication), this result is applied in an ingenious and profound manner to historical events; furthermore, in the autobiographical essays with which the volume begins, Born explains how he came to the conclusion "that the claim of classical mechanics, to be deterministic, is not justified" since there is an underlying "assumption that absolute precise data have a physical meaning, and this I regarded as absurd."

Since I have referred to Born's books on optics and atomic physics, I had better add at once that these subjects were never his fields of specialization. He himself says, in the first of the following essays, that their success "shows that in order to write a learned volume one need not specialize in the subject but only grasp the essentials and do some hard work." Few of his colleagues and readers will agree, since Born leaves out the further conditions of his gift for exposition, his dedication as a teacher, and his deep physical insight illumined by philosophical understanding. Indeed, it is these latter qualities most of all that make the following essays so profound, as it is Born's social conscience that makes them so relevant and so significant.

Even though Max Born has been a physicist's

physicist, he has also gained wide renown for one of the major popularizations of the science of the twentieth century, happily entitled *The Restless Universe,* which has introduced untold thousands of readers to the wonder and meaning of the external world as revealed by the modern physical sciences. Decade after decade, since its initial publication in 1936, and following a paperback reprint in 1951, this wonderful book has continued to delight and to inform nonspecialists by its wit and style—at once engaging and authoritative. Another exciting book, *Einstein's Theory of Relativity,* addressed to a more scientifically prepared reader, remains today one of the best introductions to relativity, although written some forty years ago.

The reader of these essays will be introduced by Max Born himself to his own scientific work and extraordinary achievement. But I may be permitted to stress one significant aspect of his thought concerning which—perhaps through modesty—he has not in my view laid sufficient emphasis. I refer to his deep philosophical insight, notably displayed in the essay, "Symbol and Reality," which is included in this volume. Author of many articles on philosophical topics, his oft-reprinted lecture, "Experiment and Observation in Physics," was a challenge to the accepted views of the nature of scientific thought. His major philosophical effort—in part an exploration of the consequences of his own scientific work—is to be found in a volume entitled *Natural Philosophy of Cause and Chance,* based on the Waynflete Lectures which he gave at Magdalen College, Oxford, in 1948. This book showed Born as the first among major scientist-philosophers to see the emptiness of positivism as a guide to our understanding of science and of our world.

In his recollections with which this book opens, Max Born states and illustrates his conviction "that theoretical physics is actual philosophy." But there is one basic difference between Born and many other theoretical physicists turned philosophers: he has from his student days read carefully in the great philosophers, and so is able to escape the traps that so often await the naïve scientist once he leaves his special domain. Indeed, Born confesses that the "philosophical background of science always interested me more than its special results." In fact, he tells us that he "never liked being a specialist and always remained a dilettante, even in what were considered my own subjects."

Readers of these recollections will discover the reasons why Max Born "never learned nuclear physics properly and could not take part in its development." As a result, he says, he "did not become involved in nuclear fission and its application to the atomic bomb." He believes that this special situation enables him "to consider the ethical and political questions" associated with the atomic bomb "from a disinterested and objective standpoint." It is in fact to these questions that most of the essays in the present volume are addressed.

The activities I have been describing may be comprised under such heads as: teaching science, explaining science, training scientists, exploring the meaning or significance of science. But, of course, Max Born's major activity, and the primary foundation of his fame and authority, has been in creating science. He is one of the founders of quantum mechanics, perhaps the major intellectual achievement of the twentieth century, comparable only to such other great achievements in scientific thought as the Newtonian philosophy and the system of dynamics on which it is based, or the great Darwinian revolution with its vast implications for biological science as a whole and our view of man's place in nature. For his part in creating the new quantum mechanics, Max Born was awarded (in 1954) the Nobel Prize in Physics. I shall not further summarize his contributions, since he has done so in an admirable manner in "What I Did as a Physicist," even explaining why it took twenty-eight years for his contribution to be fully accepted.

During the past two decades, and especially since his retirement as Tait Professor of Natural Philosophy (or, physics) at Edinburgh, Max Born has been devoting his energies more and more to the complex problems which science, through its applications, has been putting to our society, notably through the actual and potential uses of nuclear energy in peace and in war. Basically, and in different forms, Born is concerned with two major questions. First, can human affairs be regulated without the use of force? Second, can the current decline in ethics and morality be reversed? In other words, simply and directly, is there any hope for man's future?

In the first essay on these topics, "Development and Essence of the Atomic Age," Born gives the reader at once the essential basis in scientific fact and theory to understand the especially destructive force of nuclear energy, and he leads the reader beyond any simple advocacy of "prohibition of atomic weapons" to the statement that "the human race can only be saved by renouncing the use of force once and for all." In a second essay, "Man and the Atom," Born explores the relevant question of whether the march of science and the technology based upon it follows a historical regularity, "an inescapable necessity, like a law of nature itself." If so, there would be little point in "our endeavor to direct" technical progress "and give it a reasonable purpose." So Born is led, quite naturally, to: "first, the question of the existence of regularities or laws in history—for research and technology are historical phenomena—and secondly, the ancient problem of necessity and freedom." From "the standpoint of a philosophically minded physicist," Born answers these questions in a new and wholly unexpected way, of the greatest importance for all who concern themselves in any way with the problems of history or the analysis of society. The reader is left in no doubt, as Born says explicitly in another essay, "Europe and Science," that "the ethical problems which have arisen from the enormous increase in power available to man are perhaps even closer to my heart than the scientific and political ones." Among the purposes, therefore, for which these essays have been written, the paramount one is to warn all men, not only political leaders, that the greatest danger for the future of mankind may be the existence of "men who refuse to admit that the new age, upon whose threshold we now stand, is fundamentally different from all past ages."

Max Born's position oscillates between the darkest pessimism of despair and the optimism of hope that is possible only to one who has been willing to accept reality as it is and see what possibilities—if any—may exist for the future. In these essays, the troubled reader will find no easy escape from the threat that hangs over us all since Hiroshima and Nagasaki. But Born differs from many of his fellow scientists in the depth of his philosophical understanding. For example, in "Symbol and Reality," he warns us "to be careful that scientific thinking in abstract terms does not extend to other domains where it is not applicable," and to remember that "human and ethical values cannot be based on scientific thinking." The fact of the matter is, "However attractive and satisfactory abstract thinking is for the scientist, however valuable his results for the material aspect of our civilization, it is most dangerous to apply these methods beyond the range of their validity, to religion, ethics, art, literature, and all humanities."

What then, if any, is the special role of the scientist? A partial answer is given in the essay "Blessings and Evils of Space Travel." Born concludes that so-called space travel (really not travel into the immense spaces of the universe as such, but only at most "a thrust into the planetary system") is "a triumph of intellect but a tragic failure of reason." This splendid apothegm is illuminated for us in the following gloss: "Intellect distinguishes between the possible and the impossible; reason distinguishes between the sensible and the senseless. Even the possible can be senseless." We may not necessarily agree with Born that there are no values to science in the current space effort, or at least none that are commensurate with the enormous costs. But no one will deny that he is correct in declaring that the space race is currently "a symbol of a contest between the great powers, a weapon in the cold war, an emblem of national vanity, a demonstration of power." Since it is sponsored for military advantage, Born finds space research being "used directly as a preparation for war, a dangerous game."

This example may illustrate the maximum hope that men of science may use their knowledge, their enormous prestige, and their political power to inform their fellow men and continually to arouse the conscience of the world to the fundamental problems, which are ethical or moral. In a final essay, "What Is Left to Hope For?" Born traces the changes since World War I in extending warfare to civilians and noncombatants, in the constantly increasing use of force, and in the spread of moral paralysis in the face of the actual and potential destruction of innocent men, women, and children as an act of policy. "What is there left to hope for?" . . .

> The only thing that can save us is an old dream of the human race: world peace and world organization. These were regarded as unattainable, as utopian. It was believed that human nature is unchangeable, and since there had always been war there would always be war.
>
> Today this is no longer acceptable. Universal peace in a world that has become smaller is no longer

utopian but a necessity, a condition for the survival of the human race. . . .

Our hope is based on the union of two spiritual powers: the moral awareness of the unacceptability of a war degenerated to mass murder of the defenseless and the rational knowledge of the incompatability of technological warfare with the survival of the human race.

Max Born concludes with an exhortation: "But we must hope!" He contrasts two sorts of hope: one that has no influence whatever on what happens (as hoping for good weather) and another in which hope itself "is a moving force" (as "in the coexistence of people, especially in politics"). For he is convinced: "Only if we hope do we act in order to bring fulfillment of the hope nearer." Surely, "We must not tire of fighting the immorality and unreasonableness which today still govern the world."

As we read these essays, we too may find hope: in that so wise and thoughtful a man has reminded us of fundamental issues of morality and has raised his mighty voice—reinforced by the authority and prestige of his scientific position—in behalf of humanity.

I. BERNARD COHEN

PART I

How I Became a Physicist

I was born in 1882 in Breslau, the capital of the Prussian province Silesia. My father was teaching anatomy at the university, but his main interest was in research in embryology and in the mechanics of evolution. I grew up in a cultured home in a strongly scientific atmosphere. When we were very young my sister and I used to visit our father at his laboratory, which was full of instruments, microscopes, and microtomes, among other things. Later I was allowed to listen to discussions with his scientific friends, several of whom became famous: Paul Ehrlich, the discoverer of salvarsan and founder of chemotherapy; Albert Neisser, the dermatologist who discovered the gonococcus and other microorganisms. My mother died when I was a small boy and my father shortly before I left school; during his last two years he was very ill but never ceased working. His last investigations were concerned with the *corpus luteum,* and I am told by my biologist son (named Gustav after my father) that this research anticipated important modern research on sex hormones.

My school was an average German *gymnasium* where Latin, Greek, and mathematics were the main subjects. I was not particularly interested in any of them, but I remember that I enjoyed reading Homer and I still remember quite a number of lines from the beginning of the *Odyssey* by heart. In the higher forms the mathematics master, named Maschke, was not only an excellent teacher but a clever experimenter and a very kind man. He also taught physics and chemistry, for only two hours a week, and I was infected by his enthusiasm. At that time Marconi's experiments on wireless communication became known and Maschke repeated them in his little lab with me and another boy as assistants. When we succeeded in sending a signal from one room to the next he asked me to fetch the headmaster, Dr. Eckard, to show him the miracle, and I still remember our disappointment when this learned humanist remained completely indifferent and unimpressed.

Before his death my father had advised me not to specialize at once but to attend lectures at the university on different subjects and then, after a year, to make my decision. Thus I took classes, not only in mathematics and the sciences but also in philosophy, history of art, and other subjects. At first I was most attracted by astronomy. (I have given a more detailed account of my astronomical experiences in *Vistas in Astronomy*, volume 1, page 41 [London: Pergamon Press, 1955], reprinted in my book *Physics in My Generation*, page 179 [London: Pergamon Press, 1956].) But the observatory was poorly equipped; we heard nothing of astrophysics, stars, and nebulae, but only of ephemerides of planets with endless numerical computations. Soon I was fed up. Then I concentrated on mathematics and obtained quite a solid training. I am grateful to Professor Rosanes for his introduction into linear algebra, which taught me the use of the matrix calculus, later of great value in my own research.

At that time German students used to move about, spending the summer in one of the small universities in order to enjoy nature and sport, and the winter in a big city with theaters, concerts, and parties. So I spent one summer in Heidelberg, the lovely and gay town on the Neckar, and one in Zurich, near the Alps. Heidelberg did not give me much in the way of science, but there I met James Franck, who became my closest friend and years later my colleague in the physics department in Göttingen. In

Zurich I first came in contact with a first-class mathematician, Hurwitz, whose lectures on elliptic functions revealed to me the spirit of modern analysis.

The winter semesters I spent regularly in Breslau, at that time (1900-1914) a lively city with a flourishing social and artistic life. Of the numerous personal contacts which I established there I want to mention my friendship with Rudolf Ladenburg; for many years we were inseparable and spent lovely holidays together in Italy and Switzerland. He immigrated to the United States before the Nazis came to power and obtained a chair of physics at Princeton University. Among my classmates there were two who became my friends, Otto Toeplitz and Ernst Hellinger. They knew much more about mathematics and mathematicians than I did. From them I learned that the mecca of German mathematics was Göttingen and that three prophets lived there: Felix Klein, David Hilbert, and Hermann Minkowski. So I decided to make the pilgrimage. They soon followed me, and our "group from Breslau" was completed by a fourth, Richard Courant, who later became a distinguished figure in American mathematics as head of a flourishing school at New York University.

In Göttingen I attended mainly the lectures of Hilbert and Minkowski. They had been friends since their schooldays in Koenigsberg, most remarkable men, not only in their subject but in every respect. Hilbert soon offered me the rather vague job of "private assistant," unpaid but valuable beyond description by providing me with the opportunity of seeing him and listening to him every day. Often I was invited to join the two friends for long walks in the woods. Though I was accustomed to free and lively discussions among my father's biologist friends, I was deeply impressed by the way these two great mathematicians looked at the world. I learned from them not only the most advanced mathematics of the time but also something more important: a critical attitude toward the traditional institutions of society and of the state, which I have preserved throughout my life.

Here are two examples of the numerous Hilbert stories which are well remembered by his pupils and friends. Once at a party the talk turned to astrology, and some of those present were inclined to think there must be something in it. When Hilbert was asked about his opinion he said, after some deliberation: "If you were to bring together the ten wisest men in the world and ask them what is the most stupid thing in existence, they would not be able to discover anything as stupid as astrology." Another time, when Galileo's trial was discussed and somebody blamed Galileo for having failed to stand up for his convictions, Hilbert answered quite heatedly: "But he was not an idiot. Only an idiot could believe that scientific truth needs martyrdom; that may be necessary in religion, but scientific results prove themselves in due time." This kind of teaching has directed my path in life and in science.

At that time mathematics included also mathematical physics. There was, for instance, a seminar directed by Hilbert and Minkowski on the electrodynamics of moving bodies, where problems were discussed which today go under the title of relativity. This was about 1905, when Einstein's celebrated paper had appeared, although his name was not yet known in Göttingen.

My relations with Klein were not too happy. I did not like his lectures; they were too perfect for my taste. He noticed that I was often absent, and showed his displeasure. In a seminar on elasticity which he held jointly with Carl Runge, the professor of applied mathematics, I was compelled on account of the illness of a classmate to give, on very short notice, a report about a problem in elasticity, and as I had no time to study the literature I developed ideas of my own. These so impressed Klein that he suggested this problem for the annual university prize competition and wrote me that he expected me to submit a paper. At first I foolishly refused; however, as the "Great Felix" was all-powerful in mathematics, I had of course to give in: I solved the problem and won the prize. Nevertheless, I was in disgrace with Klein for a long time. Therefore I did not risk being examined by him in geometry, so I switched to astronomy. The professor was Karl Schwarzschild, the distinguished father of the famous Martin Schwarzschild of Princeton Observatory. He helped me bring my knowledge of astronomy up to date and thus I obtained my doctor's degree in 1907.

The unfortunate incident with Klein turned out in the end to be a blessing. As the paper for the prize competition had to be submitted anonymously, I could not ask advice from the professors. Thus I discovered that I was able to do scientific work on my own, and I felt for the first time the delight of finding a theory in agreement with measurement—one of the most enjoyable experiences I know.

The teaching of physics was also stimulating. The theoretical physicist was Woldemar Voigt. I attended his lectures on optics and took his advanced course in optical experiments. They were excellent and gave me a solid foundation in optics. Many years later (1922), when I was invited by Albert Michelson to give a lecture course on relativity at the University of Chicago, I used all my free time for spectroscopic work with Michelson's wonderful gratings.

How I Became a Physicist

Again years later, armed with this knowledge, I wrote a successful textbook on optics (in German; Berlin: Springer, 1933) and many years afterward another (in English; in collaboration with E. Wolf [London: Pergamon Press, 1957]). This shows that in order to write a learned volume one need not specialize in the subject but only grasp the essentials and do some hard work.

I never liked being a specialist and have always remained a dilettante, even in what were considered my own subjects. I would not fit into the ways of science today, done by teams of specialists. The philosophical background of science always interested me more than its special results. I listened to philosophical lectures, e.g., those of Edmund Husserl in Göttingen, but joined neither his nor any other school.

Of the many young scholars I met I want to mention only two. Constantine Caratheodory was a brilliant mathematician of Greek origin. He and I discussed among other things the strange fact that the rather abstract science of thermodynamics was founded on technical concepts, i.e., on "heat engines." Could this not be avoided? Some years later Caratheodory found a new, accurate, straightforward access; he published it in *Mathematische Annalen* in a rather general and abstract manner, but the paper hardly received notice. Fifteen years later I made an attempt to popularize his theory by a simpler presentation in *Physikalische Zeitschrift,* but without success. Only now, after fifty years, textbooks are appearing in which this simple and lucid approach is being used.

The second man who influenced my scientific life—though in a negative way—was Johannes Stark, who later received the Nobel Prize for his discovery of the Doppler effect in canal rays and the splitting up of spectral lines in an electric field. He was then a lecturer in physics and gave a course on radioactivity. I tried to attend it, but the presentation did not satisfy my mathematical mind and I gave up. Consequently, I never learned nuclear physics properly and could not take part in its development. I have published only one (not bad) paper on alpha decay (1929). On the other hand, another consequence was that I did not become involved in nuclear fission and its application to the atomic bomb. This enabled me to consider the ethical and political questions connected with it from a disinterested and objective standpoint.

After graduation I had to do one year of military service and was accepted by a cavalry regiment in Berlin. Here is not the place to discuss how this experience influenced my already very negative opinion of all things military. I remember correcting proofs of my prize dissertation during night watches in the stables, using the sleek back of my horse as a desk. When I got a severe attack of asthma, from which I had suffered since childhood, I was sent to a military hospital and, after some time, I was discharged. A year later I was called up again to serve in a cavalry regiment at Breslau, but was lucky enough to find that the chief medical officer was one of my father's pupils and knew my asthmatic disposition. So I was discharged again after a few weeks.

In order to learn more about fundamental problems in physics I went to Cambridge in England. There I became an advanced student at Gonville and Caius College and attended experimental courses and lectures. I found that Larmor's presentation of electromagnetism taught me hardly anything that I had not learned from Minkowski. But J. J. Thomson's experimental demonstrations were splendid and exciting. However, the most precious experiences of this period were certainly the human ones: the kindness and hospitality of the British people, the life among the students, the beauty of the colleges and of the country.

After six months I returned to my home city of Breslau and tried to improve my experimental skill. There were two professors of physics, Lummer and Pringsheim, well known through their measurements of black-body radiation. But I did not learn much from them and soon turned to theory again. I discovered Einstein's paper on relativity of 1905 and was fascinated at once. Combining his ideas with Minkowski's mathematical methods, I found a new, direct way to calculate the electromagnetic self-energy (mass) of the electron and I sent the manuscript to Minkowski.

To my great surprise he answered with an invitation to return to Göttingen and to assist him in his work on relativity.

I arrived in Göttingen in December 1908 and worked happily with him for a few weeks. Then in January 1909 he died after an appendicitis operation. All my hopes were shattered and I felt stranded. But a lecture before the mathematical society on my paper about the relativistic electron was so successful that Professor Voigt offered me a lectureship (*Privatdozent*).

So I became a resident at Göttingen for the second time. Of the great many people I met there during the following years I shall mention only a few. Among my fellow lecturers were Otto Toeplitz, Richard Courant (both mentioned earlier), and Hermann Weyl, who later became one of the stars of the Princeton Institute for Advanced Studies. To all of these I owe a great deal, but still more to Theodor von Karman, a Hungarian. He and I lived in the same house for several years, until I married (1913); we had daily discussions on physical problems, and in the course of them learned of Einstein's quantum theory of the specific heat of solids.

I had met Einstein for the first time at the scientific congress in Salzburg (1909), which is mentioned also in Lise Meitner's article "Looking Back" in the November 1964 *Bulletin of the Atomic Scientists,* and I had corresponded with him, mostly on relativity. He had already taken up Planck's quantum hypotheses in 1905, i.e., in the same year in which his first paper on relativity appeared. This paper of Einstein's introduced the idea of the light quantum or photon and gave a revolutionary explanation of the photoelectric effect and of other phenomena. In his new application of quantum theory to the thermic properties of solids Einstein used a one-oscillator model for the description of vibrations in a crystal. This led to small discrepancies between theory and experiment. Karman and I tried to eliminate these by taking account of the whole spectrum of lattice vibrations. This was a year before Laue's experiments (with Friedrich and Knipping) which showed simultaneously the wave nature of X rays and the lattice structure of crystals. Karman and I relied on the group-theoretical considerations of Fedorow and Schoenfliess, which seemed to us so convincing that even in our second paper, published after Laue's discovery, we did not quote it. This was certainly an error of judgment. It is well known that Debye anticipated our results by a few weeks, using an approximation method where no explicit use was made of the lattice structure. For years Debye's simple method was much more popular than ours.

Soon after finishing this work, Karman and I separated. He specialized in hydrodynamics and aerodynamics in which he achieved high distinction, and after his emigration (1933) became a leading figure in the United States with great influence in the air force.

I remained in physics. The work on specific heat of solids opened the two main lines of my subsequent research: lattice dynamics and quantum theory.

So now I was a physicist, which winds up the story of how I became one. But I shall add a few details of what I did in this field.

T W O

What I Did as a Physicist

I began research in 1912 with a big program: to derive all crystal properties from the assumption of a lattice whose particles could be displaced under the action of internal forces. This work took several years. The main results are the explanation of the deviations from the Cauchy relation between the elastic constants; the proof that the vibrational spectrum consists of bands of two different types, the optical and the acoustical; and the incorporation into lattice dynamics of P. Ewald's beautiful theory of electromagnetic waves in crystals.

The volume of results was so big that only a few could be published in single papers; I decided to write a systematic book. Just as the war of 1914 broke out I was offered a professorship in Berlin to take some of the burden of teaching off Planck. We moved to Berlin in the spring of 1915. I began lecturing but had to stop very soon to join the army. After a short period with the air force's wireless service I was transferred, at the request of my friend Ladenburg, to an artillery research establishment where I was attached to the department of "sound ranging"—finding the position of guns by measuring the arrival times of the reports at different places. A number of physicists worked in the same room and we soon began to do real science when time allowed. Landé and I tried to determine the internal energy of ionic crystals and succeeded with the help of Madelung, who developed a method of calculating the energy of the coulomb forces in lattices (Madelung's constant). From these results I obtained the heat of formation of simple heteropolar molecules, the first example of the determination of a chemical heat of reaction from purely physical data. In this work I enjoyed the help of the chemist Fritz Haber and the work is generally referred to as the Born-Haber theory.

During the dark days of the war (when it was hard to find sufficient food for the family) my friendship with Einstein was a great comfort. We saw each other very often, played violin sonatas together, and discussed not only scientific problems but also the political and military situation, with the lively participation of my wife. We were violently opposed to the political aims of the German government and convinced that they would lead to disaster. During these years Einstein finished his general theory of relativity and discussed it with me. I was so impressed by the greatness of his conception that I decided never to work in this field. But I defended Einstein's theory against attacks and a short time later tried to popularize it by writing a book which has appeared in a modernized version in the United States (*Einstein's Theory of Relativity*, New York: Dover Publications, 1962).

Together we experienced the military defeat, the revolution in Berlin, and the founding of the German Republic. As it was ruled from Weimar, not from Potsdam, we hoped for a peaceful future.

At that time (1919) Max von Laue, professor at Frankfurt, wrote to Planck that he longed to live in Berlin to be near his beloved teacher. He suggested exchanging places with me, and as both universities agreed, I was transferred to Frankfurt. There I had a little institute of my own, equipped with instruments; I also had the help of a mechanic. Otto Stern became my first assistant and immediately made good use of the experimental facilities. He developed the method of atomic rays for the investigation of atomic properties and used it first for the experimental verification of Maxwell's law of velocity distribution in gases and then, helped by Gerlach (assistant in the experimental department under Wachsmuth), for the investigation of the strange result of quantum theory called "quantization of direction." The Stern-Gerlach experiment is rightly considered one of the fundamental demonstrations that classical mechanics does not apply in atomic dimensions and that it ought to be replaced by a new quantum mechanics.

I also tried my hand at experimental research. With my second assistant, Miss E. Bormann, I developed a method for determining the free path of a beam of silver atoms in air. This work was later continued by a pupil of mine (F. Bielz) in Göttingen with more accurate methods and has recently been refined in several laboratories for the determination of mutual forces between atoms and molecules (e.g., by K. G. Bennewitz and J. P. Toennies in Bonn).

A. Landé, later professor at Ohio State University worked in my department as a guest. It was here that he found by ingenious numerical calculations his celebrated formulae for the fine structure of multiplets in line spectra and the so-called anomalous Zeeman effect, which became one of the empirical cornerstones of quantum mechanics.

I myself continued the work on lattice energies and their chemical consequences. The professor for physical chemistry, R. Lorenz, directed my attention to the anomalies of the mobilities of univalent ions (the bigger ones are faster than the smaller ones). I gave an explanation of these in the framework of a more extensive investigation which ought to be called electro-hydrodynamics, in analogy with the modern magneto-hydrodynamics. A mechanical effect of molecular electric dipoles was then experimentally confirmed in collaboration with my pupil P. Lertes by showing that a glass bulb filled with a nonconducting liquid was set into rotational motion by a rapidly rotating electric field.

After two years in Frankfurt, I was offered the directorship of the physics department at Göttingen, both theoretical and experimental, succeeding Peter Debye. In spite of my few experimental attempts I did not feel capable of directing a big laboratory which in my student days had consisted of two independent divisions. I succeeded in persuading the minister of education to divide the institute again and to call my old friend James Franck to Göttingen. This resulted in three institutes and three professors, Robert Pohl (who was there already as a professor "Extraordinarius"), James Franck for experimental physics, and myself for theoretical physics. This arrangement turned out very satisfactorily. We had a joint colloquium in which we alternately took the chair. My suggestion of calling Franck to Göttingen soon proved right when he and Gustav Hertz were awarded the Nobel Prize for their work on the excitation of spectra which confirmed Bohr's quantum theory of the atom (1925).

Thus, in 1921, my third period in Göttingen began under good auspices. During the first years I continued to work in collaboration with pupils on lattice dynamics. Here a new line was started in working out, together with a young, extremely gifted Hungarian, E. Brody (who perished later in a Nazi concentration camp), the thermodynamics of crystals. Sommerfeld, then editor of the physics part of the *Mathematical Encyclopaedia,* invited me to contribute a paper on the atomic theory of solids. This article took a long time to finish; it appeared later also as a book, *Atomtheorie des Festen Zustandes* (Leipzig: B. G. Teubner, 1923). My teacher, Voigt, used to derive crystal properties with the help of symmetry considerations, which are equivalent to group theory. I had the idea of applying this theory to molecules, and the work was carried out by a Dutch pupil, C. J. Brester, and published as a doctor's thesis in Utrecht. This paper is a precursor of Wigner's application of group theory to the electronic structures of atoms.

My main interest soon turned to quantum theory. In my two first assistants, Wolfgang Pauli and Werner Heisenberg, I had the keenest and most efficient collaborators imaginable. We started, of course, from the Bohr-Sommerfeld theory of electronic orbits but concentrated on its weak points where it disagreed with experience. Thus we embarked on the discovery of a new "quantum mechanics." First we tried to replace differential operations by a difference calculus containing Planck's constant; my pupil P. Jordan and I obtained some quite promising results concerning the radiation formula and other matters. Then, in 1925, Heisenberg surprised us with a new idea: starting from the principle that unobservable quantities (like the dimensions and frequencies of electronic orbits) should not be used, he introduced a symbolic calculus and obtained some promising results on simple systems (linear and nonlinear oscillators). After submitting his paper for publication I pondered about Heisenberg's formalism and discovered that it was identical with the matrix calculus well known to mathematicians. In collaboration with Jordan, the simplest features of "matrix mechanics" were established; then all three of us developed the theory systematically, with results so satisfactory that any doubt of its validity was hardly possible.

A short time later, Dirac (at Cambridge, England), also stimulated by Heisenberg's first paper, worked out quite independently a similar theory using a more general calculus of noncommuting quantities.

Then Schrödinger's papers on wave mechanics began to appear (1926). It looked as if there were now two entirely different theories; but soon Schrödinger himself was able to demonstrate their mathematical equivalence. He believed, however, that he had accomplished a return to classical thinking; he regarded the electron not as a particle but as a density distribution given by the square of his wave function $|\psi|^2$. He argued that the idea of particles and of quantum jumps be given up altogether; he never faltered in this conviction.

I, however, was witnessing the fertility of the particle concept every day in Franck's brilliant experiments on atomic and molecular collisions and was convinced that particles could not simply be abolished. A way had to be found for reconciling particles and waves. I saw the connecting link in the idea of probability. In our three-man paper, there was a section (chapter 3, paragraph 2) written by me, where a vector x with components x_1, x_2, x_3 . . . appears on which the matrices operate but to which no meaning was given. I suspected that it must have something to do with a probability distribution. But only after Schrödinger's work became known was I able to show that this guess was correct; that vector x was a discontinuous representation of his wave function ψ, and so it turned out that $|\psi|^2$ was the probability density in the configuration space. By describing collision processes as scattering of waves and by other methods, this hypothesis was confirmed. The collision theory was developed independently in a little different way by Dirac.

All this work was interrupted by a visit to America (in the winter of 1925-1926) where I lectured at M.I.T. on crystal theory and on quantum mechanics. The little volume entitled *Problems of Atomic Dynamics* (Cambridge: The M.I.T. Press, 1926; German version, Berlin: Springer, 1926) containing these lectures is, as far as I know, the first book on quantum mechanics. In collaboration with Norbert Wiener (later famous for his cybernetics) I tried to extend the matrix theory of discontinuous energy spectra to more general systems (free particles) with continuous spectra; we developed an operator calculus which came quite close to Schrödinger's method, which was at the time not yet known to us. My statistical interpretation of the ψ-function was only the first step in our understanding of the relation of particles and waves in atomic physics. The most important contributions toward clarifying the ideas were Heisenberg's uncertainty relations and Bohr's principle of complementarity. Although the overwhelming majority of physicists accepted this philosophy, there were always some who did not, among them such great figures as Planck, Einstein, de Broglie, and

Schrödinger, who had been the leaders in the first period of quantum theory. This may explain why it was twenty-eight years before I was awarded the Nobel Prize for my work (1954).

After my return from the United States, my department became a center of attraction for theoretical physicists from America and from many other countries too, among them many who later won high distinction. It was an exciting period. Apart from the official colloquium we held private discussions at my house during the evening. It was very difficult for me, a man of years, to keep up with the young ones. I made strenuous efforts but these led to a nervous breakdown (1928) which forced me to interrupt teaching and research for about a year and to go more slowly afterward. At that time of reduced activity I began to set down my lectures on optics. But instead of making a short textbook, as intended, they grew into the formidable volume which I have mentioned already.

Meanwhile the relatively peaceful twenties came to an end, and after the financial catastrophe in America in 1929 and later, Hitler and the Nazis came to power. We followed their rise with growing horror. After Hitler had become Chancellor of the Reich, we knew that there was no hope. And indeed, soon came the day when I found my name in the newspapers among those dismissed for racial reasons. We left Germany (May 1933) and found a first refuge in the Italian South Tyrol. The beauty of spring in the Dolomites was so overwhelming that we almost forgot the calamity and uncertainty of our life. Very soon invitations to many places in different countries began to arrive, among them one to Cambridge in England; this I accepted since I knew the country and the language.

Again a disaster turned out to be a blessing. For there is nothing more wholesome and refreshing for a man than to be uprooted and replanted in completely different surroundings. Even my wife, who suffered much more than I did by the expulsion from her native country, later regarded the enforced emigration as a boon. However, that holds mainly for persons with international connections. Many of my relatives and friends perished in concentration camps or committed suicide. Both my wife and I spent a considerable part of our time in Cambridge in trying to help people to emigrate. Our reception in Cambridge was very friendly. Apart from my old college, Gonville and Caius, I was attached to St. John's College, where Dirac was a fellow; the University gave me the degree of M.A. and the title of Stokes Lecturer. It was a great experience to be in the Cavendish Laboratory close to Rutherford, Wilson, Aston, Chadwick, Fowler, Oliphant, Cockcroft, and many other first-class physicists.

I worked and lectured on an idea that had occurred to me in the loneliness of the Dolomites: namely, a nonlinear modification of Maxwell's theory of the electromagnetic field where the self-energy (electromagnetic mass) of a point charge was finite. This could just as well have been discovered twenty years earlier, when it might have caused a great stir, but might also have directed theoretical research in a wrong course, away from quantum theory. In this work I collaborated with Leopold Infeld of Poland. In the end, the so-called Born-Infeld theory faded away because it could not be reconciled with quantum theory. During this Cambridge period I published a textbook, *Atomic Physics* (London: Blackie, 1935), which has now reached its seventh edition, and a popular book entitled *The Restless Universe* (London: Blackie, 1936; New York: Dover Publications, 1951).

When my appointment ended in 1936, I received an invitation from Sir C. V. Raman, head of the Indian Institute of Science in Bangalore. I accepted and with my wife spent half a year in India. This was a great experience but there is nothing to report about scientific results.

After our return to Cambridge, I received a letter

from Peter Kapitza offering me a good position in Moscow, and we considered it seriously. But a short time later my old friend Charles Galton Darwin, professor of natural philosophy—which is Scottish for physics—in Edinburgh, wrote me that he was leaving to take the mastership of a college in Cambridge and sent me the invitation of the University to become his successor.

Thus we went to Scotland and lived there for seventeen years, even longer than in Göttingen. We loved the beautiful old city, the country, and the Scottish people, and we were very happy there. However, I cannot dwell on this, but only say a few words about my work. As usual, I changed from one subject to another and found capable pupils and collaborators. I wish to mention only three of the latter. First, Reinhold Fürth, professor at the German University of Prague, who came as a refugee just before the beginning of the war and was a great help to me in directing the work of my pupils in the thermodynamics of crystals and on other topics. Next, Klaus Fuchs, a highly gifted man who never concealed the fact that he was a communist; after the outbreak of the war and a short internment as an enemy alien, he joined the British team investigating nuclear fission. I think that he became a spy not from ulterior motives but from honest conviction. The third was Herbert Sidney

Green, now professor in Adelaide, Australia, with whom I worked on a rigorous kinetic theory of condensed gases and liquids. Our papers have been collected in a little book (Cambridge: Cambridge University Press, 1941). The crystal work we did was mainly concerned with the determination of the vibrational spectra of lattices from diffuse X-ray scattering and Raman effect; an international congress recently held in Copenhagen (1963) showed that these problems are again the center of interest of solid-state physics since the use of neutrons instead of X rays has provided much more and better experimental data. We also followed up an idea of mine, called the principle of reciprocity, in different directions. Its aim was an explanation of the existence and properties of elementary particles, but it led to nothing, since the empirical material at that time was too scarce. It looks now as if these ideas are actually applicable to the newly discovered short-lived particles and resonances.

Among my students there were four highly gifted Chinese; with one of them, Kun Huang, now a professor in Peking, I wrote a new book on lattice dynamics of crystals, where quantum mechanics is systematically used (Oxford: Clarendon Press, 1954).

For all these activities I had at the beginning only two basement rooms, later three or four, and my budget was rather small compared with modern standards (in Göttingen it had been no larger). We were always rather crowded, for the number of research students was considerable; among them were few Scotsmen but people from all over the world. The administration and much elementary teaching was done by my lecturers, R. Schlapp and A. Nisbet. During the last years the staff was completed by E. Wolf, who collaborated with me on my second big optics book, *Principles of Optics* (London: Pergamon Press, 1959).

In 1948 I was invited to give the Waynflete Lectures at Magdalen College, Oxford. They appeared under the title *Natural Philosophy of Cause and Chance* (Oxford: Clarendon Press, 1949) and have been reprinted in America (New York: Dover Publications, 1965) as a paperback. In this book I tried to formulate the philosophical ideas on science which I developed during my life as a physicist.

I should like to speak about my many friends and colleagues among the professors but must restrict myself to a few. The chair of experimental physics was held by Barkla, known as the discoverer of the characteristic absorption of X rays by the elements. The head of the mathematics department was Edmund Whittaker, who often helped me in my work. The philosopher Kemp-Smith became my closest friend and taught me how to become a Scotsman, with doubtful success. In Edinburgh the work for refugees continued but was mainly done by my wife, who had joined the Quaker community. Their society, together with many other organizations, saved many hundreds of people from concentration camps and from the gas chamber. The war years in Edinburgh were as dark and depressing as everywhere else, but strangely enough we had no major air raid.

After the war, life became brighter, particularly when the city of Edinburgh started the festivals of music and drama which soon became world-famous. Many old friends appeared whom we had not seen for years, including the pianist Artur Schnabel and other artists. We were able also to visit the Continent again, and when Göttingen offered me the "freedom of the city," along with Franck and Courant, we accepted after some hesitation. This first visit to Germany was followed by others, and when, at the end of 1953, I reached the age of retirement we decided to settle in Germany. I cannot here discuss the reasons; but though some of my friends, among them Einstein, resented it, we do not regret this step. We chose a little spa, Bad Pyrmont, in a lovely countryside, not far from Göttingen but distant enough to be away from the mainstream. Here I found a new task. But before I say a few words about this, I wish to mention that I did not give up physics entirely but continued to study its philosophical implications.

On retiring from my Edinburgh chair I was awarded a *Festschrift* (honorary publication) containing a paper by Einstein, in which he presented a brief and clear argument for rejecting the statistical interpretation of quantum mechanics based on his concept of physical reality. I was unable to agree and even regarded his mathematical treatment of an example as insufficient. I wrote a reply in which I tried to justify my statistical standpoint by showing that the claim of classical mechanics, to be deterministic, is not justified because it depends on the assumption that absolute precise data have a physical meaning, and this I regarded as absurd. So I developed a statistical formulation of classical mechanics. Then I offered a forthright quantum-mechanical treatment of Einstein's example and showed that, in the classical limit, it passed over exactly into the result previously attained from my statistical formulation of classical mechanics.

Einstein replied that I had misunderstood him, as his objections had to do with the concept of reality, not with determinism. A correspondence ensued which was full of mutual misunderstandings. Pauli, who was at Princeton at the time, tried to mediate and told me frankly that I was not a good listener to other people's opinions. I suppose he was right. But he helped me to reformulate my paper, and the final version, which appeared in a number of *Transactions* of the Danish Academy in honor of Niels Bohr's seventieth birthday, met Pauli's complete approval. Although the dispute with Einstein was rather sharp, it did not in the least affect our friendship.

In Pyrmont I continued working along this line. In the end it led to the publication of a paper (with W. Ludwig) in which a formula was developed which represents the movement of a freely moving (e.g., rotating) body from the extreme quantum domain with discrete states up to the classical domain of continuity.

Now I come to my main occupation in Germany during these last years. It concerns the social, economic, and political consequences of science, primarily the atomic bomb, but also other pathological symptoms of our scientific age, like rocket research, space travel, overpopulation, and so on. When I arrived in Germany (1954) there seemed to be hardly any interest in these things. Now a society exists called V.D.W. (Vereinigung Deutscher Wissenschaftler, or Union of German Scientists) which works actively on these problems and is not without influence on the German government. A periodical called *Atomzeitalter* (Atomic Age) appears, which is similar to the *Bulle-*

tin of the Atomic Scientists. Although my publications and radio talks are often opposed to the politics of the Federal Government of Germany, I have not been hampered by it but, on the contrary, honored by an award of high distinction.

This is hardly a biography since it concerns mainly the professional events of my life and omits almost all its human aspects, my family, my relation to literature, the arts, music, and so forth. Anybody who might want to check what I have said about my work can do so in a publication which came to me as a precious honor, my *Selected Papers* in two volumes published by the Göttingen Academy (Göttingen: Vandenhoeck and Ruprecht, 1963).

THREE

———⌣———

Reflections

I should like to offer a few reflections on the meaning
science has for me and for society, and I shall intro-
duce these considerations with the very trivial remark
that achievement and success in life depend to a considerable degree on good fortune. I was fortunate
in regard to my parents, my wife, my children, my
teachers, my pupils, and my collaborators. I was fortunate in surviving two world wars and several revolutions, among them Hitler's, which was most dangerous for a German Jew.

I wish to look at science from two angles, one personal and the other general. Right from the start, as I
have already said, I found research great fun, and it
has remained enjoyable to this day. This pleasure is a
little like that known to anyone who solves crossword
puzzles. Yet it is much more than that, perhaps even
more than the joy of doing creative work in other pro-
fessions except art. It consists in the feeling of pene-

trating the mystery of nature, discovering a secret of creation, and bringing some sense and order into a part of the chaotic world. It is a philosophical satisfaction.

I have tried to read philosophers of all ages and have found many illuminating ideas but no steady progress toward deeper knowledge and understanding. Science, however, gives me the feeling of steady progress: I am convinced that theoretical physics is actual philosophy. It has revolutionized fundamental concepts, e.g., about space and time (relativity), about causality (quantum theory), and about substance and matter (atomistics), and it has taught us new methods of thinking (complementarity) which are applicable far beyond physics. During the last years I have tried to formulate philosophical principles derived from science.

When I was young, very few scientists were needed in industry. The only way they could earn a living was by teaching. I found teaching at a university most enjoyable. To present a scientific subject in an attractive and stimulating manner is an artistic task, similar to that of a novelist or even a dramatic writer. The same holds for writing textbooks. The greatest pleasure is in teaching research students. I was lucky to have had a considerable number of men of genius among them. It is marvelous to discover talent and to direct it toward a fertile field of research.

From a personal point of view, therefore, science has given me every satisfaction and pleasure a man can expect from his profession. But during my span of life science has become a matter of public concern and the *l'art pour l'art* standpoint of my youth is now obsolete. Science has become an integral and most important part of our civilization, and scientific work means contributing to its development. Science in our technical age has social, economic, and political functions, and however remote one's own work is from technical application it is a link in the chain of actions and decisions which determine the fate of the human race. I realized this aspect of science in its full impact only after Hiroshima. But then it became overwhelmingly important. It made me ponder over the changes which science has brought about in human affairs during my own time and where they may lead.

In spite of my love of scientific work, the result of my thinking was depressing. This enormous subject cannot be dealt with in a few lines. But a sketch of my life would be incomplete without at least a brief intimation of my view.

It seems to me that the attempt made by nature on this earth to produce a thinking animal may have failed. The reason is not only the considerable and ever increasing probability that a nuclear war may break out and destroy all life on earth. Even if such a catastrophe can be avoided I cannot see any but a dark future for mankind. On account of his brain, man is convinced of his superiority over all other animals; yet whether he, with his state of consciousness, is happier than the dumb animals may be doubted. His history is known for a few thousand years. It is full of exciting events but overall there is a sameness, that is, peace alternating with war, construction with destruction, growth with decline. Always there existed some elementary science developed by philosophers and some primitive technology that was practically independent of science and in the hands of artisans. Both grew very slowly, so slowly that for a long time change was hardly perceptible and without much influence on the human scene. But suddenly, about three hundred years ago, an explosion of mental activity occurred: modern science and technology were born. Since then, they have increased at an ever growing rate, probably faster than exponentially, and are now transforming the human world beyond recognition. But although this is due to the mind, it is not controlled by the mind. It is hardly necessary to give examples of this fact. Medicine has overcome most of the plagues and epidemic diseases and it has doubled the human life span within a single generation:

the result is the prospect of catastrophic overpopulation. People are crowded into cities and have lost all contact with nature. Wild animal life is vanishing rapidly. Communication from one place of the globe to the other is almost instantaneous and travel has been speeded up to an incredible extent, with the effect that every little crisis in one corner of the world affects all the rest and makes reasonable politics impossible. The automobile has made the whole countryside accessible to all, but the roads are choked and the places of recreation spoiled. However, this kind of technical miscarriage might be corrected in time by technological and administrative remedies.

The real disease lies deeper. It consists in the breakdown of all ethical principles which have evolved in the course of history and preserved a way of life worth living even through periods of ferocious warfare and wholesale destruction. It is enough to give two examples of the dissolution of traditional ethics by technology: one concerns peace, the other war.

In peace, hard work was the foundation of society. A man was proud of what he had learned to do and of the things he produced with his hands. Skill and application were highly valued. Today there is little left of this. Machines and automation have degraded human work and destroyed its dignity. Today its purpose and reward are money. The money is wanted for buying technical products produced by others for the sake of money.

In war, strength and courage, magnanimity toward the defeated foe, and compassion for the defenseless characterized the ideal soldier. Nothing is left of these. Modern weapons of mass destruction leave no place for ethical restrictions and reduce the soldier to a technical killer.

This devaluation of ethics is due to the length and complication of the path between a human action and its final effect. Most workmen know only their special tiny manipulation in a special section of the production process and hardly ever see the complete product. Naturally they do not feel responsible for this product, or for its use. Whether this use is good or bad, harmless or harmful is completely beyond their field of vision. The most horrid result of this separation of action and effect was the annihilation of millions of human beings during the Nazi regime in Germany; the Eichmann type of killers pleaded not guilty because they "did their job" and had nothing to do with its ultimate purpose.

All attempts to adapt our ethical code to our situation in the technological age have failed. The representatives of traditional ethics, the Christian churches, have, as far as I see, found no remedy. The communist states have simply given up the idea of an ethical code valid for every human being and replaced it by the principle that the laws of the state represent the moral code.

An optimist may hope that out of this jungle a new ethics will arise, and arise in time to avoid a nuclear war and general destruction. But against this there is the possibility that no solution of this problem exists because of the very nature of the scientific revolution in human thinking.

I have written about this in detail and can indicate here only the main points. (See Chapter Five, "Symbol and Reality.") The average human being is a naïve realist: i.e., like the animals, he accepts his sense impressions as direct information of reality and he is convinced that all human beings share this information. He is not aware that no way exists of establishing whether one individual's impression (e.g., of a green tree) and that of another (of this tree) is the same and that even the word "same" has no meaning here. Single sense experiences have no objective, i.e., communicable and confirmable, significance. The essence of science is the discovery that relations between two or more sense impressions, particularly statements of equality, can be communicated and checked by different individuals. If the restriction of using only such statements is accepted, one obtains an objective, though colorless and cold, picture of the world. That is the characteristic method of science.* It was developed slowly in the so-called classical period of physics (before 1900) and became dominant in modern atomic physics. It has led to an enormous widening of the horizon of knowledge, in the macrocosmos as well as in the microcosmos, and to a stupendous increase of power over the forces of nature. But this gain is paid for by a bitter loss. The scientific attitude is apt to create doubt and skepticism toward traditional, unscientific knowledge and even toward natural, unsophisticated actions on which human society depends.

* I do not think that this definition of scientific cognition is new. It is implicit in many scientists' writings. But I have not found it formulated explicitly, even by modern scientific philosophers. The problem is touched on, for instance, in the first chapter of the interesting book by Henry Margenau called *Ethics and Science* (Princeton: D. Van Nostrand Company, Inc., 1964) in the form of a controversial discussion between the author and the philosopher Northrop. But the point which I regard as essential, i.e., that objective, communicable, and confirmable statements can be made not about single sense impressions but only about pairs of these, is not even mentioned. The book aims to show that ethics can be built up with the help of methods analogous to the scientific ones. My thesis, that science and technology have destroyed the ethical base of civilization, perhaps irreparably, has, as far as I see, not been treated.

No one has yet devised a means of keeping society together without traditional ethical principles or of arriving at them by means of the rational methods used in science.

Scientists themselves are an inconspicuous minority; but the impressive successes of technology give them a decisive position in society today. They are aware of a higher objective certainty obtainable by their way of thinking, but they do not see the limitations of it. Their political and ethical judgments are therefore often primitive and dangerous.

The nonscientific mode of thought depends, of course, also on an educated minority, i.e., the lawyers, theologians, historians, philosophers, who by the limitations of their training are unable to understand the most powerful social forces of our time. Thus civilized society is split into two groups, one of which is guided by the traditional humanistic ideas, the other by scientific ones. This situation has recently been discussed by many distinguished thinkers, for example, C. P. Snow (*Science and Government,* London: Oxford University Press, 1961). They generally regard it as a weak point of our social institutions but believe that it can be remedied by a properly balanced education.

Proposals for an improvement of our educational institutions in this direction are numerous, but so far ineffective. My personal experience is that very many scientists and engineers are fairly well educated people who have some knowledge of literature, history, and other humanistic subjects, who love art and music, who even paint or play an instrument; on the other hand the ignorance and even contempt of science displayed by people with a humanistic education is amazing. Offering myself as an example, I know and enjoy a good deal of German and English literature and poetry, and have even made an attempt to translate a popular German poet into English (Wilhelm Busch, *Klecksel the Painter,* New York: Frederick Ungar, 1965); I am also familiar with other European writers: French, Italian, Russian, and others. I love music, and in my younger years played the piano well enough to take part in chamber music or, with a friend, to play simple concertos on two pianos, and occasionally even with an orchestra. I have read and continue to read books on history and our present social, economic, and political situation. I make attempts to influence political opinion by writing articles and giving radio talks. Many of my colleagues share these interests and activities—Einstein was a good violinist; Planck and Sommerfeld were excellent pianists, as are Heisenberg and many others. Concerning philosophy, every modern scientist, particularly every theoretical physicist, is deeply conscious that his work is intricately interwoven with philosophical thinking and that it would be futile without a thorough knowledge of the philosophical literature. This was a leading idea in my own life which I have tried to imbue in my pupils—not of course in order to make them partisans of a traditional school, but to make them able to criticize and to find flaws in the systems and overcome these by new concepts, as Einstein has taught us. Thus I should think that scientists are not cut off from humanistic thinking.

Concerning the other side of the matter, it seems to me rather different. Very many of those I have met whose education has been purely humanistic have no inkling of real scientific thinking. They often know scientific facts, even intricate facts of which I have hardly heard, but they do not know the roots of the scientific method of which I have spoken above; and they seem to be unable to grasp the point of such considerations. It seems to me that skillful, basic scientific thinking is a gift that cannot be taught and is restricted to a small minority.

But in practical affairs, particularly in politics, men are needed who combine human experience and interest in human relations with a knowledge of science and technology. Moreover, they must be men of action and not of contemplation. I have the impression that no method of education can produce people with all the qualities required.

I am haunted by the idea that this break in human civilization, caused by the discovery of the scientific method, may be irreparable. Though I love science I have the feeling that it is so greatly opposed to history and tradition that it cannot be absorbed by our civilization. The political and military horrors and the complete breakdown of ethics which I have witnessed during my lifetime may be not a symptom of an ephemeral social weakness but a necessary consequence of the rise of science—which in itself is among the highest intellectual achievements of man. If this is so, there will be an end to man as a free, responsible being. Should the race not be extinguished by nuclear war, it will degenerate into a species of stupid, dumb creatures under the tyranny of dictators who rule them with the help of machines and electronic computers.

This is no prophecy, only a nightmare. Though I have not taken part in applying scientific knowledge to destructive purposes, like making the A-bomb or the H-bomb, I feel my own responsibility. If my reasoning is correct, the fate of the race is a necessary consequence of the constitution of man, a creature in whom animal instincts and intellectual power are mixed.

However, my reasoning may be quite wrong. I hope so. Someday a man may appear abler and wiser than any in our generation, who can lead the world out of its impasse.

PART II

———⌣———

Development and Essence

of the Atomic Age

In discussing the atomic age, its development and
nature, I shall not enlarge upon physical discoveries
and their application to technological and military
ends, but rather trace the historical roots of these
discoveries and their consequences upon the destiny
of man. A scientist like myself has, however, little time
for historical studies. Instead, I have to rely on the
fact that during my long life I have witnessed a portion of modern history and pondered about it. And I
have read or at least scanned a few books which may
be useful for my purpose. I remember Spengler's *Decline of the West* from my student days. I have also
read a little in Arnold Toynbee's great work and listened to some of his Gifford Lectures at Edinburgh. I
mention these two authors because both share the
opinion that there are regularities or even laws in hu-

man history which can be revealed by a comparative study of various nations and civilizations. Most of what I know of European history derives, however, from a book much used at British schools and in elementary university courses because of its admirable style and clarity, H. A. L. Fisher's *A History of Europe*. His point of view can be gathered from a few lines of his preface:

> Men wiser and more learned than I have discerned in history a plot, a rhythm, a predetermined pattern. These harmonies are concealed from me. I can see only one emergency following upon another as wave follows upon wave, only one great fact with respect to which, since it is unique, there can be no generalizations, only one safe rule for the historian: that he should recognize in the development of human destinies the play of the contingent and the unforeseen. This is not a doctrine of cynicism and despair. The fact of progress is written plain and large on the page of history; but progress is not a law of nature. The ground gained by one generation may be lost by the next. Thoughts of men may flow into the channels which lead to disaster and barbarism.

There thus seem to be two historical schools, one which believes that history obeys laws and has a meaning, another which denies this.

As a scientist I am accustomed to search for regularities and laws in natural phenomena. I beg your forbearance if I consider the problem in hand from this standpoint, yet in quite a different manner from that used by Spengler and Toynbee.

The dawn of a new historical age—the transition from antiquity to the medieval period, for example —is obviously not recognized as such by those who live through it. Everything goes on without break, the life of the son is not much different from that of the father. It is the historians who have divided the past into periods and ages in order to find their way in the chaos of events. Even the beginning of the scientific-technological period in which we are living was a slow process stretching over more than a hundred years and hardly noticed by the people of that day.

Today, however, things seem to change more rapidly. During the span of a very few years something new has been discovered which is transforming our lives. This new feature simultaneously offers a horrible threat and a brilliant hope: the threat of self-destruction of the human race and the hope of earthly paradise. And this is not a revelation of religious prophets or of philosophical sages; on the contrary, these two possibilities are presented to the human race by science, the most sober activity of the mind. The threat of destruction in particular is demonstrated by the examples of Hiroshima and Nagasaki, although the atom bombs used there were children's toys compared with the thermonuclear weapons developed since.

I have not taken any part in the development of nuclear physics; but I know enough of it to realize that what it implies is not the multiplication of destructive power but a radical and sweeping transformation of the situation. The stock of A- and H-bombs in the United States and in Russia is probably sufficient to wipe out all of the larger cities in both countries, and presumably all remaining centers of civilization in addition. But much worse developments are in preparation or are perhaps already available for application: the cobalt bomb, for instance, which produces a radioactive dust capable of spreading over wide areas and killing all creatures living in the region. Particularly sinister are the aftereffects of radioactive radiation on generations unborn: mutations may be induced which could lead to a degeneration of the human race. The useful applications of nuclear physics—the generation of energy, the production of isotopes as instruments in medicine and technology—may indeed become a blessing in the future, but only if there is a future. We are standing at a crossroad, the like of which the human race has never before encountered.

This "to be or not to be" is however only a symptom of a state in our mental development. We must inquire into the deeper cause of the dilemma in which man has become involved.

The fundamental cause stems from the discovery that matter, of which we and all things around us are made, is not solid and indestructible, but unstable and explosive. Quite literally, we are all sitting on a powder keg. To be sure, this keg has rather strong walls, and we required a few thousand years to drill a hole in it. But today we have done it, and we may at any moment blow ourselves sky-high. This dangerous situation is simply a matter of fact. I shall return to the scientific background later and describe it in rather more learned terms. But first I want to discuss whether it would have been possible to let the keg remain untouched and to sit peacefully on it without caring about its content. Or, without the use of this metaphor, could the human race not have lived and flourished without investigating the structure of matter and thus conjuring up the peril of self-destruction?

The answer to this question presupposes a definite philosophy of history. I am hardly entitled to claim any knowledge in this field; I shall therefore attempt to approach it with the methods of a scientist.

Viewed from this aspect the situation appears to be this: man is often defined as a "thinking animal";

his development depends on his ability to accumulate experience and to act accordingly. Single individuals or groups lead the way, others follow and learn. For centuries this was an anonymous process: we know nothing of the men who invented the first tools and weapons, who learned cattle breeding and agriculture, who developed languages and the art of writing. But we may be sure that even then there took place the eternal struggle between the minority of innovators and the conservative mass that we observe in the written documents of all later periods. The total number of men increases with each improvement of the conditions of life. If the percentage of the gifted remains roughly constant, their absolute number grows at the same rate as the total number of men. And with each technical invention the possibility of new combinations increases. Hence the situation is similar to that of the calculus of compound interest; one has what the mathematicians call an exponential increase.

Of course, this is correct only in very broad terms; it is a statistical law. But I am convinced that the laws of statistics are valid in history just as in the game of roulette or in atomic physics, in stellar astronomy, in genetics and so forth; in short, in all cases where one deals with large numbers. We know today that most of the laws of nature are of a statistical kind and permit deviations; we physicists call these fluctuations.

As this idea is not familiar to everybody, allow me to illustrate it by a simple example. The air which we all breathe seems to be a thin, continuous substance of uniform density. But investigations with intricate instruments have shown that actually the air consists of innumerable molecules (mainly of two kinds, oxygen and hydrogen) which fly about and collide with one another. The appearance of continuity is a consequence of the grossness of our senses, which register only the average behavior of large numbers of molecules. But then the question arises: why is the average distribution uniform in the chaotic dance of molecules? Or in other words: why is there an identical number of molecules in two equal volumes of space? The answer is that there is never exactly the same number of molecules in equal volumes, but only approximately the same number; and this is the consequence of a simple result of statistics, according to which this approximately uniform distribution has an overwhelming probability as compared with any other. But there are deviations which can be observed if the two volumes compared are sufficiently small. Particles suspended in the air—for instance, pollen from plants or cigarette smoke—perform tiny irregular zigzag motions which can be seen in a microscope. The explanation given by Einstein for this effect, called Brownian movement, is simply that the number of air molecules hitting such a tiny but microscopically visible particle in opposite directions is not exactly equal in any short time interval; hence the particle is pushed about through the fluctuations of the averaged recoil. In principle there is no limit to the size of these fluctuations, but a statistical law makes it extremely improbable that very large deviations will occur. Otherwise it might happen that the density of the air near my mouth might become so small for a few minutes that I would suffocate. I am not afraid of this because the probability of its occurring is infinitesimally small.

Even the degree of uncertainty follows certain defined statistical rules. I think that history in the cosmic sense is subject to the same statistical law. But ordinary history deals generally with small groups and relatively short periods of time; in these circumstances, it is not the statistical uniformity but the fluctuations which strike the eye and appear chaotic and senseless. If one observes a nation or a group of peoples over a period of, say, a few hundred years, nothing of that "statistical development" may be visible; indeed there may even be signs of retrogression. But sooner or later the power of the human spirit will manifest itself in another part of the world and at another time. One conclusion seems therefore inescapable: the process of gathering and applying knowledge as an endeavor of the whole human race over long periods of time must follow the statistical law of exponential increase and cannot be halted.

A few historical examples may illustrate this point. The decisive step on the way to atomic physics was made about twenty-five hundred years ago, in the speculations of the Greek school of natural philosophy, by Thales, Anaximander, Anaximenes, and especially the atomists Leukippos and Democritos. They were the first to think about nature from a pure desire for knowledge, without seeking an immediate material advantage. They postulated the existence of natural laws and tried to reduce the variety of matter to the configuration and motion of invisible, unchangeable, equal particles. It is not easy to apprehend the immense superiority of this idea over all conceptions current at that time in the rest of the world. Together with the magnificent achievements of Greek mathematics, this idea might have produced a decisive scientific-technological advance, had the social conditions been more favorable. But the Greek gentlemen lived in a world which venerated the harmony and beauty of body and mind; they despised manual labor as the task of slaves and they neglected experiment, which cannot be carried out without the risk of soiling one's hands. Thus no empirical verification of the ideas was attempted, nor were they applied technically, although if they had been, the ancient world might have been spared the assault of the barbarians.

After the great migrations, the Christian Church erected a system ill-disposed to innovation. Yet the fire kindled by the Greeks smoldered under the ashes. It lay hidden in the books which were kept and copied in many monasteries or stored in the libraries of Byzantium, and it flared up to a bright flame in the Arabian scholars who guarded the Greek tradition until the time came for it to be rediscovered and who even created essentially new things in mathematics and astronomy. The Byzantines who fled before the Turks to Italy brought with them their books and, more important, not only the knowledge of classical antiquity but also the idea of research. Thus came the time of discovery and invention which secured Europe's dominance for a few centuries.

There are two conclusions to be drawn from these considerations. First, it is quite absurd to believe that the crisis in the existence of the human race, brought about by the dawn of the atomic age, could have been avoided or the further development of dangerous knowledge inhibited. Hitler tried to choke off what he called "Jewish physics," the Soviets tried the same with Mendelian genetics, both without success and to their own detriment. Secondly, the seeming suddenness of the appearance of the critical situation is mainly an illusion of perspective. The knowledge of nature and the power springing from it have been steadily growing—if with fluctuations and retrogressions—with the increasing acceleration characteristic of a self-supporting (exponential) process. Thus the day inevitably had to come when the change in the conditions of life produced by this process would be considerable during one single generation, and therefore would appear as a catastrophe. This impression of catastrophe is increased by the fact that certain nations have not taken part in this technical development and have to adapt themselves to it without preparation.

Our generation is gathering the harvest sown by the Greek atomists. The final result of physical research is a confirmation of their fundamental idea that the material world is essentially composed of equal elementary particles whose interaction produces the variety of phenomena. Those elementary particles are called nucleons, because by clotting together they form the atomic nucleus. The chemical atoms are neither indivisible (as the name indicates) nor identical in the same chemical element, as believed during the last century. This is a consequence of the fact that a nucleon may be either electrically neutral—in which case it is called neutron—or it may carry a positive elementary charge—in which case it is called proton.

Development and Essence of the Atomic Age

The chemical atoms consist of a nucleus which is an extremely dense agglomeration of neutrons and protons (hence it is positively charged), and an extended cloud of negative electric particles, called electrons, surrounding the nucleus. Atoms which have the same number of protons and therefore the same number of electrons in the cloud are chemically and in most respects also physically indistinguishable, even if the number of neutrons in the nucleus differs. Such almost identical atoms, which differ only in the number of neutrons, that is, in their mass (weight), are called isotopes.

The lightest element, hydrogen, consists mainly of one isotope, the single proton. The next heaviest element, helium, consists mainly of an isotope having two protons and two neutrons. When these fuse, energy is liberated—a great deal of energy in fact. The process does not occur spontaneously because in order to bring the four particles together some energy has to be expended. The situation is like that of a dam, the gates of which have to be raised before the water in the reservoir can stream out. The same holds for the consecutive elements in the chemical table; they are potentially unstable and would combine unless there were barriers, fortunately very strong, to keep them apart. This is the case in the series of elements up to the middle of the whole system; from there on the situation is reversed, each nucleus having the tendency to split and only prevented from doing so by a barrier. The heaviest of the elements found in nature, uranium, has the weakest barrier, and it was this which was first broken artificially by the experiments of Hahn and his collaborator Strassmann in 1938.

The way from these delicate laboratory experiments to the first uranium reactor (or pile) which was built in Chicago by Enrico Fermi in 1942 was long and demanded an enormous amount of ingenuity, courage, skill, organization, and money. The decisive discovery was that the fission of a uranium nucleus produced by the collision with a neutron is accompanied by the emission of several neutrons, and that the process could be directed in such a way as to produce an avalanche of new fissions, in short, a self-sustaining reaction. The reverse process, the fusion of light nuclei into heavier ones (for example, hydrogen into helium) is the source of energy of the sun and of all stars. In the central parts of these the temperatures and pressures are so high that the combination of four nucleons is possible through a chain reaction in a series of steps. The same fusion has now been accomplished here on earth by using a uranium bomb as a detonator. And so now we have the H-bomb.

There is no longer any doubt: all matter is unstable. If this were not true, the stars would not shine, there would be no heat and light from the sun, no life on earth. Stability and life are incompatible. Thus life is necessarily a dangerous adventure which may have a happy ending or a bad one. Today the problem is how the greatest adventure of the human race can be directed to a happy end.

It may be appropriate, for this reason, to say a few words about the blessings which can be obtained if men behave reasonably. There is, first of all, the problem of energy. When I was young, half a century ago, it was estimated that our coal reserves would last a few hundred years; oil was not used then on a large scale. Since then, an enormous amount of coal has been burned, oil has been discovered and used at an ever increasing rate. Yet the estimate of the duration of the fossil fuel reserves is still many hundred years. It may not seem to be an urgent problem therefore to find new sources of energy. But this conclusion would be erroneous. Coal and oil are not only sources of energy but the most important raw materials for innumerable chemical products. Think of plastics and their numerous applications. There will come a time when the agricultural output does not suffice for feeding the ever increasing number of human beings. Then chemistry will be challenged to produce substitutes, for which coal is the only available raw material. Hence it seems dangerously wasteful to utilize coal and oil simply for burning. Moreover, the social aspect of the question must not be forgotten. The day seems not far away when in civilized countries no workmen will be willing to take up the dark and dangerous profession of a miner, at least not for economically bearable wages. England already seems to be approaching this state of affairs. Then there are many countries which have neither coal nor oil; for these the easily transportable nuclear fuel will be a blessing.

Another type of peaceful application of nuclear physics makes use of the radioactive by-products of atomic reactors. Unstable, i.e., radioactive, isotopes of many elements are produced which can be applied to many purposes: as sources of radiation, instead of the expensive radium, in medicine, technology, agriculture; for the treatment of cancer, the testing of materials, the production of new species of plants through mutations and perhaps most importantly as "tracer elements." By adding a small amount of radioactive isotope to a given element it is possible to follow the fate of this element in chemical reactions, even in living organisms, by observing the radiation emitted. An ever increasing number of experiments in biological chemistry are already using this method which marks a new epoch in our knowledge of the processes of life.

All this, with what may develop in the days to

come, offers great prospects. An international conference at Geneva has discussed the exploitation of all these possibilities through the collaboration of all nations. I am not a nuclear physicist and did not attend it. I hope the labors of this meeting will yield a rich harvest. However, I still ask myself whether even a technical paradise can counterbalance the evil of the atomic bomb. For when I used the words "paradise on earth" in the beginning, I meant not technical progress, but the realization of the eternal yearning of man for "peace on earth."

In regard to the rest of the opinions I wish to express, I cannot rely on my knowledge of physics, nor on my sporadic studies of history; they seem to me just common sense, and they are shared by a number of friends, leading scholars from different countries. We believe that a major war between great powers has become impossible, or at least will become impossible in the near future. For it would lead, in all likelihood, to general destruction not only of the fighting nations but also of the neutrals. Clausewitz' well-known saying that war is the continuation of policy by other means no longer holds true, for war has become insanity; and if the human race is unable to renounce war, its zoological name should not any longer be derived from *sapientia* but from *dementia*.

The leading statesmen seem to be well aware of

this situation. The decline of tensions which we are observing is an indication that it is so. The fear of the enormity of the catastrophe which might be the result of an armed conflict has led everywhere to negotiations. But fear is a bad foundation for the reconciliation and solution of conflicts. Is it conceivable that the peace resting on fear which we very likely are attaining at present may be replaced by something better and more reliable?

I shall have to take the risk that you regard me as a slightly ridiculous fellow who refuses to acknowledge an awkward situation

> *Because, he argues trenchantly,*
> *What must not happen cannot be,*

as the grotesque philosopher Palmström says in *Songs from the Gallows,* by the German poet, Morgenstern.*

However, I am not alone in my hope for a lasting peace. Einstein shared this hope, and just before his death gave it clear expression in a joint statement with Bertrand Russell and others. Eighteen Nobel laureates, chemists and physicists, gathered for a scientific dis-

---

* Christian Morgenstern wrote deep and beautiful poetry, which, however, found little resonance in the public. Then he published several little volumes of grotesque, apparently senseless verse under the title *Galgenlieder,* in which he caricatured his philosophy through two strange figures, Palmström and Korff. These books had a tremendous and lasting success.

cussion at Lindau, unanimously accepted a declaration (the Mainau Statement) along similar lines. And many other people and groups of people have published similar declarations. But not much time is available for their words to take effect. Everything depends on the ability of our generation to readjust its thinking to the new facts. If it is unable to do so, the days of civilized life on earth are coming to an end. And even if all goes well, the way will pass very, very close to the abyss.

For the world is full of seemingly insoluble conflicts: national frontiers are displaced, populations expelled; there are conflicts among races, languages, national traditions, religions; the colonial system is bankrupt; and finally, there are the opposing ideologies of capitalism and communism. Can we really hope that all these terrible tensions will be solved without application of force? Would it not be preferable, instead of pursuing the radical proposition to abandon war, to make an attempt to prohibit the new weapons of mass destruction by international agreement? My friends and I consider this idea impracticable for the following reasons:

The production of energy through nuclear reactions is already being planned on and improved everywhere. A system of supervision intended to inhibit the production of weapons of destruction can function only in peacetime. If war between major powers should break out, even if it were initially conducted with conventional weapons, the supervision would cease. Is it reasonable to assume that a nation in distress but believing that it could save itself with the help of the atom bomb would be willing to renounce this last resource?

As for the "conventional weapons," I must confess that I am unable to understand why they are not causing the same horror which is generally felt today with respect to the atomic weapons. They have ceased to be honorable weapons used by soldiers against soldiers; instead they have become means of indiscriminate destruction. They are directed not only against military objects but also against the whole organization and productive capacity of the enemy nation, against factories, railways, houses; they kill the helpless and the old; they destroy the most noble and irreplaceable achievements of civilization. From the moral standpoint the decisive step toward modern barbarism was the concept of total war. Even without atomic weapons, the prospect of the effects of using ordinary bombs, in combination with chemical and bacteriological poisons, is appalling enough.

Prohibition of atomic weapons alone is not justified, either morally or by the actual facts. The human race can only be saved by renouncing the use of force once and for all. Today fear has produced a precarious state of peace. The next aim must be to stabilize this peace by strengthening the ethical principles which alone can secure the peaceful coexistence of man. Christ has taught how man ought to behave toward man. The nations have up to now acted—and the churches have not objected to this attitude—as if these commandments were valid only within their own borders, but not in regard to their relations with one another. That is the root of the evil. We can only survive if in the international sphere distrust is replaced by understanding, jealousy by the will to help, hatred by love. In our time, before our eyes, the doctrine of nonviolence has been victorious in the hands of a non-Christian, Mahatma Gandhi, who liberated his country without war (and I do not think that he would have acted differently if his adversaries had not been the well-meaning British, but any other nation). Why should it not be possible to follow his example?

One often hears hard words about the atomic physicists: all calamity is the fault of these "athletes of the brain," not only the atom bomb but also the bad weather. I have endeavored to show that the development of the human mind was bound to lead one day to the disclosure and application of the energy stored in the atomic nucleus. That this happened so quickly and so thoroughly as to produce a critical situation is the consequence of a tragic historical accident; the discovery of the fission of uranium happened just at the moment when Hitler acquired power, and in the very country where he acquired power. I, like many others, had to leave Germany then; and I have seen the panic which struck the rest of the world when Hitler's initial successes made it appear possible that he might subjugate all nations of the globe.

The physicists who emigrated from Central Europe knew that there would be no salvation if the Germans were the first to produce the atomic bomb. Even Einstein, who had been a pacifist all his life, shared this fear and was persuaded to warn President Roosevelt. The scholars who emigrated from Europe contributed much to the uranium project; the most prominent of them was Enrico Fermi, one of the greatest physicists of our time. No blame can be attached to the men who constructed the atom bomb unless one accepts the teaching of extreme pacifism that power should never be used even against the greatest evil. The use of the bombs against Japan in the last phase of the war seems to me a different matter. Responsible for it are not only politicians and soldiers, but the group of scientists who advised the committee appointed by President Truman to decide the question. These men were swallowed up by their problems and triumphant when a solution was found; but they pondered little about the consequences of the results. And if they did so, it was with the feeling that it was beyond their sphere of influence. The idea of abandoning research because its effects might be dangerous seemed absurd to them and seems so to their successors; for if they gave up there would be plenty of others to continue, and if the Americans were not on top, the Russians would be. Almost all have returned to peaceful occupations, to research and teaching, and they desire nothing better. Societies have been formed among them to discuss and study the social responsibility of scientists and to oppose the misuse of the discoveries.

There are of course a few physicists who have tasted power and liked it, who are ambitious and want to preserve the influential positions acquired during the war. But I think that on the whole, the ideal of politics without force will be less resisted by scientists than by other social groups. Even the ambitious and worldly scientists will be satisfied with directing big projects of development. The consequences of the appearance of this type of man for the development of science itself is outside the frame of this discussion. May I express my personal opinion that from the standpoint of fundamental research their appearance may turn out to be deplorable, perhaps disastrous. A new Einstein is hardly to be expected in such an environment. On the other hand, an admixture of scientists in politics and administration seems to me an advantage, because they are less dogmatic and more open to argument than people trained in law or classics. To illustrate this let me record a personal experience.

There was the usual yearly gathering of Nobel laureates—chemists and a few physicists—at Lindau, Lake Constance, in July 1955, for the discussion of scientific problems. Otto Hahn, Werner Heisenberg, and I submitted to them a declaration (the Mainau Statement) prepared by us in collaboration with some other scholars of different countries, in which the dangers of the present situation were emphasized and the abandonment of war demanded. Most of the participants agreed at once, but a few had doubts. A famous American scholar objected: "I have just come from a visit to Israel and convinced myself that the existence of this little nation can be secured against the pressure of the Arabs only by the force of arms." That is plausible enough. But in the end he accepted our arguments (the same as given here) and he signed the declaration with the rest of us.

Exactly the same objection is made wherever the recent wars have left painful wounds, where boundaries have been shifted, populations expelled—as in Israel, Korea, Southeast Asia, Germany. I myself have experienced enough to know what it means to be the

Development and Essence of the Atomic Age

victim of political persecution. I was allowed to return to my home country, Germany, but my proper homeland, Silesia, is now a part of Poland. That has been a painful loss, but fate has decided. To endeavor to redress the situation by force would be impossible without condemning us to much worse injustice and very likely general destruction. We have to learn resignation; we have to practice understanding, tolerance and the will to help, and we must renounce threats and the use of force. Otherwise the end of civilized man is near.

For I believe that Bertrand Russell is right: our only choice is between *co*-existence and *non*-existence. Let me end by quoting his words:

> For countless ages the sun rose and set, the moon waxed and waned, the stars shone in the night, but it was only with the coming of Man that these things were understood. In the great world of astronomy and in the little world of the atom, Man has unveiled secrets which might have been thought undiscoverable. In art and literature and religion, some men have shown a sublimity of feeling, which makes the species worth preserving. Is all this to end in trivial horror because so few are able to think of Man rather than of this or that group of men? Is our race so destitute of wisdom, so incapable of impartial love, so blind even to the simplest dictates of self-preservation, that the last proof of its silly cleverness is to be the ex-

termination of all life on our planet?—for it will be not only men who will perish, but also the animals and plants, whom no one can accuse of communism or anti-communism—I cannot believe that this is to be the end.

If we all refuse to believe this, and act accordingly, it will not be the end.

———— ◦◦ ————

Man and the Atom

To begin with a special case, let me say a few words about myself and the atom. We, the atom and I, have been on friendly terms, until recently. I saw in it the key to the deepest secrets of nature, and it revealed to me the greatness of creation and the Creator. It supplied me with satisfactory work, in research and teaching, and thus provided me with a livelihood. But now it has become the source of deep sorrow and apprehension, to myself as well as to everyone else.

Since the destruction of Nagasaki and Hiroshima the atom has become a specter threatening us with annihilation. We ourselves have conjured up the genie, it has served us faithfully for a while, but now it is insubordinate. How has this come about? Should we not have anticipated that the creature bred by us could one day outgrow us and become dangerous? Would it then not be better to have nothing to do with it? Or is it still in our power to tame it and to use it as our servant?

These are the questions which I wish to discuss and to try to illuminate. They are fundamental questions for the human race. I cannot answer them, but I can express a few ideas, some of which the atom itself has taught us; we must keep these ideas in mind if we wish to master it. The word "atom" as used here does not stand for the tiny particle that, when assembled in large numbers, exerts prodigious forces, but for the science that has discovered this particle and its cumulative power. And the word "man" not only stands for the rational being that has created atomic science and harnessed atomic power, but also for the man in the street, who knows nothing of all this and who reads in his newspapers of a danger which he does not understand.

In fact, it is only in a manner of speaking to say that the atom has become dangerous, or that the atomic physicists have brought its danger into being. The source of the danger is in all of us, because that source is the weakness and passion of ordinary human beings.

Therefore, the physical and technical aspects will play only a small part in my considerations. I shall deal with human problems, both historical and political. However, I am a physicist, and in thinking about history and politics I cannot help using methods which I have learned in my science. True science is philosophical; physics, in particular, is not only a first step toward technology, but   way to the deepest layers of human thought. Just as three hundred years ago physical and astronomical discoveries dethroned medieval scholasticism and opened the way for a new philosophy, today we are witnessing a movement which, starting from apparently insignificant physical phenomena, leads to a new era in philosophy. It is just this way of thinking, rooted in atomic physics, that may contribute to an understanding of the dangers of the atomic age and thus to avoiding them.

Deadly dangers they certainly are. The human race has today the means to self-annihilation—either in a fit of complete lunacy, i.e., with one swift blow in a world war, or by careless handling of atomic technology, through a slow process of poisoning and of deterioration in its genetic structure.

Was this development unavoidable? Were human beings not able to live well enough without probing into the mysteries of the structure of matter which led to the danger of self-destruction? In more general terms, is technical progress, based on the knowledge of natural laws, an inescapable necessity, like a law of nature itself?

If this be true, what sense could there be in our endeavor to direct it and to give it a reasonable purpose? Had we not rather accept a fatalistic attitude and live blithely from day to day?

We have, therefore, two questions to answer: first, the question of the existence of regularities or laws in history—for research and technology are historical phenomena—and secondly, the ancient problem of necessity and freedom.

Before discussing the actual situation today and the prospects for the future, I propose to consider these two general problems from the standpoint of a philosophically minded physicist.

Very few historians are inclined to agree that the events which are dealt with in history books exhibit regularities of the kind that can be put into the form of laws of nature. There are the well-known theories of Spengler and of Toynbee, who claim to have discovered periodicities in the vicissitudes in the life of peoples, nations, and civilizations—processes of growth, maturity, and decay, like those which occur in plants and animals. I cannot judge whether this is correct, and it does not matter here, as I have in mind quite a different type of regularity, which appears whenever large numbers of objects are involved: namely, statistical—or better, stochastic—laws. (The word "stochastic" is used today when a system composed of numerous particles changes its state in consequence of random actions and interactions.) To treat these regularities properly one has to use the calculus of probability, invented by Blaise Pascal, so that he might be able to understand games of chance. From gambling, this calculus has spread widely into many other human activities. Today it is applied, for instance, to insurance, to research into industrial production, to the distribution and regulation of traffic, and to many other fields. It is also used in many branches of science, for example, stellar astronomy, genetics, epidemiology, the distribution of species of plants and of animals, and so on.

In physics, statistical methods are closely related to the atomistic idea which first appeared in chemistry as a useful hypothesis, long before there was any evidence of the real existence of atoms; and which was then applied to explain the properties of gases. The movements of a single atom in a gas are too complicated to be followed in detail; and, moreover, they are of no interest. There is the need to explain relationships between observable quantities, like density, pressure, temperature, which are *averages;* therefore, the kinetic theory of gases was developed with the help of statistical methods, and out of this development grew the more general theory of statistical mechanics, which is applicable also to other states of matter. But this theory differs from all other applications of statistics to nature in one essential point, indicated by the word "mechanics." The laws of mechanics as founded by Galileo and Newton are strictly causal and deterministic. The motion of atoms is subject to these laws. Hence, the movement of atoms in a gas is a process which combines regularity with randomness. Physics has succeeded in reconciling these two features in the imposing structure called the statistical theory of heat.

Let us now return to the historical problem of the development of science and technology. There the situation appears to be somewhat similar. Consider a close-knit association of human beings, of the kind that existed in older historical periods: a community, a state, or a group of nations. The individual in such a community follows the impulses of his will and is simultaneously subjected to the influences of his surroundings and of his neighbors. When we consider the behavior of a large number of individuals in a community, we will observe a mixture of psychological and statistical regularities which are analogous to those of statistical thermodynamics. In this way, we obtain the following picture:

The development of a civilization is carried forward by a minority of the population, namely, by those who are gifted, curious, keen, and who are discontented with the situation in which they find themselves. They show the way; the masses follow. It is reasonable to assume that the percentage of gifted persons in a population remains roughly constant. Every improvement of the conditions of life implies an increase in the total population, and, at the same time, also an increase in technical possibilities. Hence, on the average, the rate of progress must be proportional to the degree of civilization which exists at any given time. That means that the average increase of the degree of civilization must follow an exponential law. This is a simple stochastic law, which must hold for the development of any healthy closed community.

Against this reasoning it may be argued that the concept of the "degree of civilization" is much too vague for such a definite statement to be made about it. It is true that for ancient periods of history, there seems to be no possibility of checking the postulated law. But in the—particularly interesting—modern phase, investigations have been made which fully confirm the exponential law. I shall mention only those which have come to my knowledge by chance, thanks to Derek J. de Solla Price, professor of history of science at Yale University. He has found methods for measuring the degree of development in science and technology, for example, by counting the numbers of research papers published per year, or the number of persons employed in a trade, profession, or industry, and so on. He found an exponential increase, often with amazing accuracy (about 1 per cent), and at an equally amazing rate, corresponding to doubling every ten to fifteen years. The evidence on which these results are based dates back roughly to the year 1700, which is the beginning of the modern scientific age. At the same time, the observations also demonstrate the limits of the validity of the exponential law: it is interrupted by external disturbances, such as the wars of 1914-1918 and 1939-1945, which produced clear deviations from the exponential curve representing the number of publications in physics (taken from *Physical Abstracts*). But more important than these obvious disturbances are other deviations. If the objects considered belong to a larger but finite class, e.g., the schoolteachers in a community of people, an exponential increase can occur only as long as the number of these objects is a fairly small fraction of the whole class. If the fraction becomes too large, the exponential group turns into a less rapid (e.g., a linear) one; or it stops altogether. Counterreactions then develop, among which certainly not the least is the will of man, directed by reason (that is to say, not all citizens can be allowed to become teachers).

I am inclined to think that these special investigations, however restricted in scope, give an image of the development of civilization as a whole. Yet, in making this generalization, one has to take into account the fact that humanity as a whole consists of numerous groups of nations which were once totally inde-

Man and the Atom

pendent and which still behave as if they were independent, but which have quarreled, fought wars, and destroyed one another. These processes, which from my present point of view (macro-history) appear as disturbances, are the subject of ordinary history (micro-history). They have slowed down scientific and technological progress, often for long periods, but they have not succeeded in stopping it. There is no doubt that this statement is true for that long—overwhelmingly long—period known as "prehistoric," during which the half-animal, apelike creature developed into a civilized man, with language, writing, agriculture, cattle breeding, tools, weapons, houses, villages, towns, and so on. When we turn to the period covered by written history, we hear more of wars, devastations, and catastrophes, because these are more striking and exciting than normal growth. But, averaged over all the nations of the earth, the increase in the degree of civilization is undeniable. From 1700 on, it has become rapid and breathtaking. In the end, it has led to the discovery of atomic forces and of nuclear energy, and, in this way, to a crisis in the life of the human race.

In my opinion, therefore, the question whether this crisis of existence could have been avoided must be answered with a definite "No." A short review of the history of atomic science will confirm this conclusion.

Atomic science began about 600 B.C. with the speculations of the Greek philosophers Thales, Anaximander, and Anaximenes, who were the first to think about nature, impelled by sheer curiosity and the desire for knowledge, without an immediate practical aim. The atomists Leukippos and Democritos postulated the existence of laws of nature and tried to reduce the variety displayed by different substances to the configuration and movement of invisibly small, unchangeable, indivisible particles, the atoms.

This fascinating, beautiful, and inspiring idea about the essential nature of matter was buried in oblivion for a long time, for no means were available for producing evidence in favor of it. Even the general idea, that it is possible to confirm theoretical constructions by systematic experimentation, had first to be grasped and developed. The Greeks themselves greatly contributed to this. We owe them not only the foundation of abstract mathematics, but also its first applications to nature, e.g., the statics of rigid bodies and liquids, and the Ptolemaic system of the celestial bodies.

Greek civilization was destroyed by invasion from outside. But the Arabs took up and preserved the scientific tradition of the Greeks. They transmitted it to the peoples of Europe, who became the leaders in science from the sixteenth century onward. However, it should not be forgotten that there were periods during which science flourished also in China and in India.

Attempts to throttle science have been made very often. The Roman Catholic Church burned Giordano Bruno at the stake and condemned Galileo Galilei. In our own time, during Hitler's rule, we heard the slogan of "Jewish physics," which led to the expulsion of many physicists from Germany and so to a decline in German physics. The Soviets rejected the Mendelian laws of genetics and persecuted its adherents for several years; in the end, they had to give up.

Returning now to the idea of atoms; it reappeared in chemistry (apart from some primitive attempts in the kinetic theory of gases) at the beginning of the nineteenth century, through the work of John Dalton. A little later, the idea spread to physics, at first through the definitive formulation of the kinetic theory of gases. From there we can see a straight pathway of development to the nuclear atom of today.

The most important point reached on the way was the discovery that the atom actually has no right to its name—which means "indivisible"—but that it is built up of smaller elementary particles. How this happened I can indicate only briefly. The discovery of X rays by Roentgen and of radioactivity by Becquerel opened the way. Almost at the same time, in the mid-nineties of the last century, came the discovery of the electron by J. J. Thomson and about fifteen years later that of the atomic nucleus by Rutherford. The period that followed was mainly devoted to the investigation of the arrangement and movement of the electrons which surround the nucleus like a negatively charged cloud. It turned out that classical mechanics was unable to deal with these structures and that it had to be replaced by quantum mechanics, of which I shall say a few words later. Finally the investigation of the atomic nucleus itself was taken up. The result was a confirmation of the old Greek concept of the existence of ultimate particles. Today we call them nucleons and distinguish between two kinds, the protons and the neutrons, according to whether they are electrically charged or not. An atomic nucleus is formed through the aggregation of nucleons; the number of positively charged protons determines the nuclear charge and thereby the number of negative electrons in the outer cloud which are necessary for electrical neutrality; the chemical nature of the atom depends only on the number of electrons. But a nucleus with a given number of protons can still contain different numbers of neutrons; consequently atoms exist which are chemically identical but have different masses; they are called isotopes.

In 1938, Hahn and Strassmann found that when a uranium isotope absorbs a neutron it becomes unstable and splits into two parts of almost equal size. The detailed investigation of this "fission" process revealed that a few neutrons are emitted at the same time; if other uranium nuclei are hit by these neutrons, a chain reaction results which sets free an enormous amount of energy.

In 1942 a group of physicists in Chicago led by Enrico Fermi succeeded in constructing a reactor (or "pile") in which this process went on in a controllable manner.

At this point, I am tempted to allow some free play to my imagination: how would things have turned out if there had been no war at that time? I presume that everything would have gone in essentially the same way, though somewhat slower. The first reactor might have been built five or ten years later, somewhere in the civilized world. The politicians and military leaders would, of course, have got wind of the thing. But the difficulties and expenses of producing an atomic bomb are so gigantic that it may be doubted whether anything would have been achieved without the acute pressure of war. The Western parliaments would have hesitated before voting colossal sums for a project whose feasibility could only be proved on paper. There might have been time to consider the consequences and to attempt an international arrangement for avoiding the danger of atomic war.

But it did not happen like that. The process was accelerated by a historical accident, like a chemical reaction by a catalyzer. The accident consisted in the fact that the discovery of nuclear fission was made in Germany during the initial period of Nazi rule.

I had to leave Germany, like many others, and I have witnessed the terror that engulfed the rest of the world when Hitler's initial successes made it appear possible that he might subjugate all the peoples of the world. Had Germany been able to construct an atomic bomb before the other nations there would have been no salvation. Even Einstein, a pacifist all his life, shared this fear and was persuaded to warn President Roosevelt. That was the beginning of a startling development. Enormous means were provided, a gigantic organization was created, and the best scientific and technical brains set to work. The result was the first explosion of an atomic bomb at the experimental station at Alamogordo in the United States (July 1945).

Up to this point everything went quite "normally," in view of the political situation: the politicians and soldiers were acting with circumspection according to their duty; and the physicists, chemists, and engineers performed their national service in the task where they were most useful; they were having unlimited means available for the investigation of a new, fascinating branch of science and were promoted in the social scale to the rank of VIP's.

The tragic turn was the decision to use the new weapon by dropping two bombs on densely populated Japanese cities. Who was responsible for this decision? President Truman gave the order after listening to many advisers. Among these were not only politicians and soldiers but also leading scientists. It is true that a group of atomic scientists gave warning and correctly predicted the consequences in a report sent to the Secretary of War; the report bears the name of the chairman of the committee, James Franck, my old friend and colleague of bygone peacefull times in Göttingen.* But another group of eminent physicists were in favor of the dropping of the bombs.

I have used the word "responsibility"—not "guilt." For who would be presumptuous enough to judge men who, under the stress of war, acted according to their best knowledge and conscience? The justi-

* The Franck Report appeared in the *Bulletin,* 1 (May 1, 1946), 2-4, 16.

fication for the perilous decision usually offered is that it brought the war to an earlier end and saved the lives of hundreds of thousands of soldiers, not only Americans but also Japanese. We avoid mentioning the hundreds of thousands of Japanese civilians—men, women, and children—who were sacrificed. Or, if they are mentioned, it is said that their destruction was not essentially different from what all belligerents were doing in ordinary air attacks. And indeed, this cannot be denied. But can a great crime be justified by the statement that we are accustomed to committing many smaller crimes?

I am not afraid to use the word "crime," but I shall not call any single person a criminal. What we are concerned with is collective guilt, the decay of our ethical consciousness, for which we are all to blame, myself included—though I have had nothing to do with the development of nuclear physics. A few of my colleagues in different countries will agree with me, but many more will contradict me sharply and say: "That is sentimental nonsense"; or "You have to serve your country and not ask questions"; or "You have convinced yourself that all this has been a necessary development, hence spare us your moral indignation."

The last objection is a serious one: how can you speak about guilt and collective crime when you have recognized the inevitability of the development from the savage with bow and arrow to the airman with an atomic bomb?

It would be hopeless to appeal to a hard-boiled, materialistic scientist directly by way of ethical or religious arguments. But there is a way of reasoning which is based fundamentally on evidence taken from the atom itself. I have already said that atomic physics has taught us not only about the material world, but also a new way of thinking. It has given us an epistemological lesson which, when properly interpreted, becomes a philosophy, a doctrine of living. I want to give you a brief outline of what I mean.

Let us return from the world stage to the study and the laboratory of the scholar. I have explained how classical physics was transformed through atomistics. The original rigid causal laws of Newtonian mechanics had to be supplemented by probability considerations to permit the proper treatment of gases and other systems composed of many atoms. For this purpose, statistical mechanics and the kinetic theory of heat were developed. It was still thought, however, that the particles, if only their movement could be observed in detail, would obey the same mechanical laws as do the planets, the positions of which can be predicted thousands of years ahead. But, as the investigation of the structure of the single atom progressed, it became clear that the electrons in the cloud surrounding the nucleus did not obey the classical laws of mechanics. The first hint that we had struck something entirely new was given by Planck's quantum hypothesis in 1900. During the following twenty-five years these beginnings grew into modern quantum mechanics, which brought order and meaning into the chaos of atomic phenomena. I cannot enter here into a discussion of this theory. I want to stress only one point: the new mechanics makes, *in principle,* only statements of probability. It does not answer the question, Where is a particle at a given instant? but only the question, What is the probability for a particle being at a given time at a certain place? The new theory is thus less apodictic in its prediction and in a way more modest than the old theory. This change of attitude was due to the recognition that every observation implies an interference with, and a perturbation of, the thing that is observed. Therefore the data used in classical mechanics to predict the course of a movement are in principle unobtainable—the laws of nature themselves prohibit it. This restriction of measurability is the essence of Heisenberg's well-known uncertainty relations. Moreover, we have learned to describe one and the same process with the help of quite different images or models, without becoming involved in contradictions. A radiation—for example, a beam of light or a cathode ray—can be described either in terms of a train of waves or in terms of a rain of corpuscles, according to the method of observation. The compatibility of these apparently contradictory descriptions is ensured by the fact that both are contained in a single, rigorously correct mathematical theory. To describe this situation, the great Danish physicist Niels Bohr introduced the expression "complementarity." It applies to two different aspects of the same physical situation, both useful for its intuitive understanding. In its totality, however, the process can be comprehended only with the help of the mathematical theory.

Bohr has generalized this epistemological lesson into a "philosophy of complementarity." There are many domains of human thought where one and the same fact can be seen from different but complementary aspects. For instance, in biology, physicochemical methods are used for the investigation of living organisms, but no biologist would refrain from describing the processes of life in an entirely different language, which operates with concepts such as purpose, order, development, and so on. Both forms of expression may be used side by side as long as one is aware of the limits of their validity: the deeper the physicochemical analysis of a biological process, the more is the process itself disturbed, and this suggests that the mechanism of life cannot be wholly established because the process of investigation would destroy life itself.

The most audacious application of the idea of complementarity is Bohr's solution of the ancient problem of necessity and freedom. We believe in natural laws and rely on their validity in everyday life. But we human beings are part of nature and subject to her laws. Therefore what we do should be just as predetermined as any natural process. But we regard ourselves as creatures capable of forming opinions and of acting on the basis of free decisions; we therefore pass judgment on human actions, calling them good or bad, just or unjust. How can we do so if every human action is nothing but part of a predetermined, automatic process? The contradiction seems insoluble. Only two possibilities seem to exist: either one must believe in determinism and regard free will as a subjective illusion, or one must become a mystic and regard the discovery of natural laws as a meaningless intellectual game. Metaphysicians of the old schools have proclaimed one or the other of these doctrines, but ordinary people have always accepted the dual nature of the world. Bohr's idea of complementarity is a justification of the common people's attitude, because it directs attention to the fact that even an exact science like physics has reconciled itself to the use of complementary descriptions, which provide a true image of the world only when they are combined.

I am convinced that Bohr is right, and therefore I am not afraid to regard certain features of human history as governed by laws, and at the same time to speak of responsibility and guilt.

With this physical-philosophical digression, I shall now return to those contemporary events that came about as a result of the collision of atomic science with politics.

During the years since the first atomic explosion, the alliance directed against Hitler has dissolved and the cold war between the two groups of states usually called East and West has begun.

How little the essence of scientific knowledge has penetrated into men's consciousness was revealed by the period that followed the end of the war. Many American politicians believed that the technical advantage of the West could be preserved by secrecy. The effect of this was to hinder the progress of research on their own side and, through the ensuing witch hunt, to bring about a serious danger to those civil liberties which are the pride of their country. Nothing could prevent the Russians from confirming a known fact of nature and from exploiting it technically. The explosion of their first uranium bomb in 1949 broke the

American monopoly, and when the development of the hydrogen bomb began, the Russians drew level with the West.

The hydrogen bomb is based on quite a different nuclear process from that used in the uranium bomb, for, instead of the fission of heavy nuclei, use is made of the fusion of light ones: a helium nucleus is produced from two protons and two neutrons. It is well known that this reaction is the source of the energy of the stars, which they radiate into space. It is the process which keeps the sun shining and so makes life on earth possible. In the central regions of the stars, temperature and pressure are so high that the fusion process goes through a chain of intermediate reactions. Similar conditions of temperature and pressure can now be produced on earth by using a uranium bomb for ignition, and the result is the so-called thermonuclear explosive device. The energy set free in such an explosion can be a thousand times greater than in the case of a uranium bomb, and it is possible to make bombs of any size, and comparatively cheaply. The hydrogen bomb is an absolutely devilish invention, and there was opposition to its manufacture in the United States. The man who directed the production of the first uranium bomb, Robert Oppenheimer, tried to prevent the production of the hydrogen bomb, but without success. He was expelled from the Atomic

Energy Commission of the American government. The principal promoter of the hydrogen bomb was Edward Teller, who not only developed its theory but also agitated for its production. Thus he has inscribed his name in the book of world history—whether on the debit or on the credit side the future will reveal. Teller's own justification, of course, is this: if we do not make this bomb, the Russians will. As a matter of fact, the first H-bomb explosion in Russia took place only a short time afterward. Both of these men, Oppenheimer and Teller, as well as Fermi and other participants in this work, including some of the Russian physicists, were once my collaborators in Göttingen long before all these events, at a time when pure science still existed. It is satisfying to have had such clever and efficient pupils, but I wish they had shown less cleverness and more wisdom. I feel that I am to blame if all they learned from me were methods of research and nothing else. Now their cleverness has precipitated the world into a desperate situation.

Both camps, East and West, have a sufficient number of bombs to destroy mutually all big cities and industrial centers by means of airplanes and guided and ballistic missiles. I shall make no attempt to compete with novelists and journalists in describing the horror of atomic war. Yet, it is necessary to remember that the unrestricted application of atomic weapons would lead not only to the destruction of specific targets, but also to the radioactive poisoning of the atmosphere, which would spread over the whole globe. Even the few experimental bombs which have been exploded for "research" purposes in remote corners of the earth have significantly increased the radioactivity of the atmosphere. Following actual nuclear warfare, not much would be left of our civilization. The survivors of the bombs would suffer agonizing death through radiation sickness: friend and enemy, belligerent and neutral, animal and plant life.

The leading statesmen of the big atomic powers are in the habit of declaring that a great war has become impossible. But neither their own foreign offices nor the governments of smaller states take much notice of such declarations. The old diplomatic game, the bargaining and quarreling about small advantages, continues as if nothing had happened. The reluctance of the great powers to be involved in serious conflict is used by smaller nations for blackmail. East and West are pursuing atomic armament because they distrust one another and are under the illusion that they can gain security by intimidation. The word "war" is avoided, but warlike actions, the breaking of international law, and the application of brute force are perpetrated under other guises—as we have witnessed in Hungary and in Egypt.

Man and the Atom

Immensely costly preparations for war are constantly being made, which must under no circumstances be allowed to come about.

Such is the insane situation in which we find ourselves. It looks as if our civilization were condemned to ruin by reason of its own structure. The literature and philosophy of our time reflect this situation: I am thinking of the novels of Aldous Huxley and George Orwell, and of the writings of the existentialist philosophers.

There is no doubt that the human race is in an acute crisis. At the present time, fear alone enforces a precarious peace. However, that is an unstable state of affairs, which ought to be replaced by something better.

We do not need to look far in order to find a more solid basis for the proper conduct of our affairs. It is the principle which is common to all great religions and with which all moral philosophers agree; the principle which in our own part of the world is taught by the doctrine of Christianity; the principle which Mahatma Gandhi had actually carried into practice.

Fifty years ago, when I was young, this statement would have been regarded as utopian and foolish. To-day, I am able to express it without raising doubts as to my sanity. It is very likely that tomorrow, not the pacifists, but the bellicose will be regarded as fools, for the experiences of the last fifty years have left an indelible impact on the minds of men. Yet, I feel unequal to the task of analyzing and discussing this immense problem in all its aspects. What can I add to the words of the great poets and prophets of our time? I have in mind the address given by Albert Schweitzer when he received the Nobel Peace Prize; the declaration published by Albert Einstein, a short time before his death, together with Bertrand Russell and other scholars of many nations; the Mainau Statement signed by fifty-two Nobel laureates; and many other similar declarations. Today, these voices no longer die away unheard, for the man in the street—and perhaps also some of the great of this world—listens to them.

I am not blind to the difficulties of current policies: the conflict of interests and the clash of ideologies, of races, and of religions. But when in human history have such problems ever been solved by war? Usually, one war has only led to the next one. Is there any possible political aim which would justify the risk of atomic war? There are a great many politicians and journalists who reply to the warnings of the experts with catch-words such as "atomic hysteria," and "bomb defeatism." Such politicians and journalists are either shortsighted or fanatics and therefore evil, or else they represent one of the numerous groups of people to whose advantage it is—or seems to be—that wars are planned or even fought. Such people are the industrialists who profit from the production of armaments; soldiers who like military life with its romantic tradition, and who prefer blind obedience to personal responsibility; officers, generals, admirals, and air marshals, whose profession is the preparing and fighting of war; and, lastly, physicists, chemists, and engineers who invent and manufacture new kinds of weapons. It is impossible to stabilize the present state of precarious peace based on fear, without giving these people other aims in life.

There is no general recipe for doing this. However, I am able to say a few words about the physicists, whose mentality is known to me. I do not think that there is a single one among them who could be compared to Herostratos, the citizen of Ephesus, who put fire to the temple of Diana in order to achieve immortal fame. Among some of the physicists who worked on new weapons, ambition was certainly one of the motives. None of them, of course, had the desire to destroy for the sake of fame, but they did wish to contribute to the defense of their own country and of its ideology. The physicists are not the mysterious, sinister figures they are represented to be in a certain popular literature, but ordinary people gifted with a particular talent. Their ethics have nothing to do with their science. They regard as good what is beneficial to their country, just as all other citizens do. But at the same time they are strongly conscious of a particular mission—and this leads me to a question of supreme importance which I have so far omitted from my consideration.

The discovery of nuclear energy is not only a threat, a danger to the existence of mankind, but also the means of deep penetration into the secrets of nature, and thereby of technical progress. It is, indeed, without exaggeration, the salvation of human civilization from another creeping danger, namely, the exhaustion of the fossil fuels—coal and oil.

The atomic reactors produce not only explosives but also two other things which are of the utmost importance: radioactive isotopes and energy.

A discussion of radioactive isotopes would be beyond the scope of this essay, and therefore I shall say only a few words about them. As far as I can see, there are four important fields for the application of radioactive isotopes: (1) As natural clocks in the investigation of geological, cosmological, and archaeological chronology. (2) As highly sensitive indicators or "tracers," to show the presence and the movement of various substances in physical, chemical, metallurgical, and physiological processes. (3) As a means of accelerating the rate of mutations and thereby producing new species of organisms for theoretical study of genetics and practical use in agriculture. (4) As a powerful tool in medical diagnosis and therapy, particularly in the treatment of cancer. Each of these fields has been revolutionized by the use of isotopic methods; much has been achieved already and much more can be expected. But all this belongs only indirectly to my subject.

The question of energy production, however, bears on my subject directly. Our civilization rests entirely on the exploitation of the fossil fuels, coal and oil, with a small contribution from water power. These fuels are at present still being produced—or rather, extracted—from their limited deposits in sufficient quantity. But the day is approaching when the output will not equal the demand, as I have shown earlier.

The demand for energy—and that for foodstuffs too—must increase at least at the same rate, and actually increases considerably faster than the world population, since the populations of vast territories, mainly in Asia and Africa, still live under conditions which lag far behind those of the more advanced countries, and are keen to catch up.

Since the total store of fuel is limited, one needs no great gift of prophecy to predict the approach of a fuel crisis for civilized man.

How the long-term problem of the supply of food is to be solved, is probably unknown even to the experts in nutrition; but as to the problem of the supply of energy, the discovery of methods for liberating nuclear energy has come just in time to avert a catastrophe. The deposits of uranium and thorium are sufficient for many generations, even if the demand for energy, made by the backward nations, should increase to the level of those made by the Europeans, Americans, and Australians. Vigorous research is also being directed to the problem of how to make the fusion of hydrogen a controllable reaction; the raw material for this process is available in unlimited quantity. The technical difficulties, such as the removal of radioactive waste products, are great, but presumably surmountable.

The atomic physicists are conscious of their responsibility for this development, without which our civilization would collapse miserably from lack of energy; and they are working devotedly in order to solve the scientific, technologic, economic, and social problems connected with the new source of energy. But these special problems are outside my subject, which is how mankind as a whole is reacting to the new situation.

It is as if fate were putting man to the test, saying to us: You want to live, to increase in number, and to improve your conditions—I am giving you the key to your future, but on one condition: that you give up your quarrels, suspicions, and brute force. If you refuse, woe betide you.

Will the warning be heeded?

There are indications that it will. To begin with, among those in my own profession, the feeling of social responsibility is growing. In the United States and in Great Britain, societies have been formed which oppose the misuse of science for war. The work on the peaceful applications of nuclear physics is being done by international cooperation. In 1955, a big conference in Geneva was devoted to this purpose, and in 1956, official delegates from many countries met in New York in order to found an international organization. I wish to quote a few words from the admirable address given by Niels Bohr to the Geneva meeting: "It is the very difficulty of appreciating the traditions of other nations on the basis of one's own national tradition that requires that the relationship between cultures may rather be regarded as complementary." Free acknowledgment of differences, and substitution of enmity between peoples by the sense of their complementarity: this is the way in which a great abstract thinker urges reconciliation upon the nations, before an audience of scientists from all parts of the world.

Among Christians, there should be no need for such abstract formulations. It should be sufficient to take the teaching of Christ seriously and to measure good and evil not with a national but with a human gauge. Never in history was this demand so pressing, never the punishment for refusing it so obvious.

These considerations have naturally led to powerful propaganda for the abolishment of nuclear weapons by international agreement. To be frank, I do not think much of these efforts. For even if a war between great powers should break out and be conducted initially with conventional weapons—with increasing stress, no nation can be expected to renounce the use of any weapon it may see necessary for its salvation. In fact, military leaders in the United States have declared they would not wait for extreme emergency, but that in case of attack they would strike at once against the Eastern bloc with nuclear weapons. I am convinced that the only way to avoid general destruction is the general renunciation of the use of force in political conflict, combined with progressive disarmament. Instead of the propaganda for the prohibition of atomic weapons, I recommend a vigorous campaign of enlightenment about the nature of total war. The beautiful notion of the hero who fights and dies for his country, his wife, and his child is out of date. Very likely, wife and child will be victims of the atomic bomb long before the soldier, who is better protected in his dugout or tank; and the mother country, after being saved from aggression, will look like a landscape on the moon.

Now if we assume that in the future the great powers will avoid war, at first from fear, and later perhaps from worthier motives, and that they will prohibit or at least restrict warlike conflicts between minor nations, what kind of a peace will it be?

Hardly a comfortable peace, a paradise on earth, of which I, like many others, have often dreamed. Even if organized and industrialized mass murder were to cease, there will be no end to conflict, because of the iron law which nature has decreed for all living beings. Science and technology will then follow their tendency to rapid expansion unhampered, and in an exponential fashion, until saturation sets in. But that does not necessarily imply an increase of wealth, still less of happiness, as long as the number of people increases at the same rate, and with it their need for food and energy. At this point, the technical problems of the atom touch social problems, such as birth control and the just distribution of goods. There will be hard fighting about these problems; if not with deadly weapons, then with the more civilized weapons of the mind. Even if the specter of the atomic bomb is successfully exorcised, the specter of the exponential growth will see to it that a completely carefree and peaceful life will never be achieved. In the background there will always be the danger of self-destruction through the release of nuclear energy, as punishment for relapse into political barbarism.

We have witnessed with horror such a relapse. For once, we have been saved by the reaction of public opinion throughout the world: public opinion—that means ourselves. And every one of us can contribute to its becoming more powerful every day.

Europe and Science

To look upon Europe from the standpoint of a scientist is no easy task, for science is intrinsically international. The only way, I found, was to present not physics, or the history of physics (which is mostly European), but the history of the world (and the position of Europe in this history), as seen by a physicist. I will use a method for which we physicists are notorious, but whose extraordinary success in science cannot be denied: the method of mental simplification by emphasizing one single point of view. I will look at the multicolored picture of history through colored glasses which permit me to see only one— but a fundamentally important—aspect of it. In this way, one loses in richness but gains in clarity.

Let us look at Europe from the point of view of technological development. I believe that it is legitimate to consider, as a decisive factor in human history, the kind of energy mankind had at its disposal at a given time. From this point of view, history contains two—and only two—great periods: one from Adam to our time, the other from now into the future. The transition between the two is the change from the use of solar energy to purely terrestrial energy.

I consider this transition—in the midst of which we find ourselves today—an event of immense importance, beyond all comparison with any previous event.

All energy on earth is derived ultimately from processes which take place in the nuclei of atoms. All life on earth is supported by the radiation sent out from the surface of the sun, and the latter, in turn, is derived from the energy released by nuclear processes in the interior of the sun.

Until recently man had no other energy at his disposal except that coming from the sun in the form of solar radiation, and stored either in the atmosphere or in plants. This was the first period of history as viewed from the point of view of energetics. This period is further divided into three clearly separable chapters, one from beginning of history to the advent of firearms, the second from the advent of firearms to the invention of the steam engine, the third from the invention of the steam engine to the construction of the first nuclear reactor in the fateful year 1942.

I would like first to consider very briefly the physical aspect of the subject. Everyone now knows that matter consists of atoms. Their diameter is only one ten-millionth of a millimeter. "Atom" means "indivisible" in Greek; but the physical atom carries this name unjustly, because it is not indivisible. The atom consists of an extremely small, positively charged nucleus, surrounded by a cloud of negative electrons. The number of these electrons is such as to make the atom as a whole electrically neutral. The mass of an electron is about eighteen hundred times smaller than that of the lightest nucleus—that of hydrogen. The latter is called a proton; and its charge differs from that of the electron only in sign. The nuclei of other atoms are dense packages of protons and neutrons; the latter are uncharged particles with almost exactly the same mass as the protons. It is now customary to refer to protons and neutrons together as the "nucleons." Nuclei having a certain number of protons must be surrounded by an equal number of electrons, independently of their content of neutrons. Such atoms, though they may have different masses, appear identical from the outside. They are called isotopes. Chemical elements are, in general, mixtures of several isotopes.

All physical and chemical properties of matter result from processes in the electron clouds of atoms; while radioactive processes—natural and artificial— take place in the nuclei. The nuclei are shielded from the outside by the electron clouds; it was only recently that physicists first succeeded in penetrating them. The linear dimensions of the electron clouds are about ten thousand times greater than those of the nuclei. The energy stored by the binding of the outer electrons to the nucleus is, inversely, very much smaller (a hundred thousand or even a million times smaller), than that stored in the binding of nucleons in the nucleus.

I have often been asked why it is that the smallest particles carry the largest energy. The precise analysis of this relation would lead us too far. It is perhaps sufficient to refer here to the well-known Newtonian law of attraction, which says that two masses (such as the sun and a planet) attract each other with a force inversely proportional to the square of their distance. The work required to separate two mutually attracting bodies so far apart that the attraction force becomes negligibly small is what we call the "binding energy" of the bodies before the separation. From Newton's law one can derive that the binding energy of two massive bodies is inversely proportional to the distance between them. If the earth could be moved to an orbit with half its present diameter, its binding energy to the sun would be twice as large as it is now.

Coulomb's law says exactly the same about the electric forces which act between charged particles, whether they are attractions or repulsions. Since both protons and electrons are charged particles, one sees immediately that the contribution of electric forces to the total energy of the protons, compressed closely together in a nucleus, must be many times higher than the binding energies of the electrons, which are much farther removed from each other and from the nucleus.

This, however, is not the whole story. Since protons are all positively charged, they repel each other. For a structure such as a nucleus to exist at all, forces of a different type must be present, which produce an attraction between all nucleons. These forces must be restricted to a very short range.

There is one aspect to the discovery of these forces which has to do with the European theme. The experimental elucidation of atomic structure was an achievement of Europe and America. The theoretical interpretation of this structure (the reduction of experimental facts to simple fundamental laws) was almost entirely European. It is impossible to name all those who contributed to it without writing a history of modern physics. I will mention only two names: Ernest Rutherford, whose experiments first revealed the structure of atoms—the existence of nuclei and electron clouds; and Niels Bohr, who created the theory of the structure of the electron clouds and derived the above-mentioned factor of ten thousand from known natural constants. In the elaboration of Bohr's general principles into a quantitative theory of atomic structure, the two central ideas of modern physics, Einstein's theory of relativity and Planck's quantum theory, played a decisive role. Their importance reaches far beyond natural science into philosophy.

It is characteristic of our time that the interpretation of short-range nuclear forces, with the help of the two last-named fundamental theories, was the work of a non-European, the Japanese physicist Yukawa (1935). His theory opened to physics entirely new, broad perspectives, by suggesting the existence of short-lived elementary particles with masses intermediate between those of the electron and of the proton (and therefore called "mesons"). Several such particles have been discovered since then. The study of these particles, which is likely to provide the key to the mystery of the fundamental components of matter, will probably remain the central task of physical research in its next stage.

It is perhaps no exaggeration to assert that of all the products of the human mind, theoretical physics has been (besides polyphonic music) the most exclusively European of all, having no counterpart in other civilizations. This monopoly was broken by Yukawa.

With this excursion into physics, let us now return to a consideration of history from the point of view of energetics.

When I was studying physics and astronomy sixty-five years ago, the origin of the enormous energy which stars continually send out into space was a great unsolved mystery. All physical processes known at that time—for example, the conversion of gravitational energy into heat through contraction (suggested by Helmholtz)—were quite insufficient to supply the needed energy. Radioactivity was a new discovery at that time, and soon physicists began to suspect that radioactive processes—nuclear transformations in the interior of the stars—could supply the needed energy. However, only in 1938 did Bethe and von Weizsäcker independently find the correct specific interpretation of these processes.

Small nuclei are unstable because they have a tendency to coalesce into larger ones with the liberation of energy. For example, the next heaviest nucleus after hydrogen, that of helium, consists of two protons and two neutrons. It is, however, so unlikely that these four minute particles would ever meet in the same moment that even in the extremely compressed matter in the interior of a star such events practically never occur. The four particles can, however, get together in a very roundabout way, with the aid of some heavier nuclei acting like catalysts in chemistry. Bethe and von Weizsäcker first identified this sequence of reactions.

Like all stars, our sun radiates into space energy derived from this "fusion" process of hydrogen nuclei. A minute fraction of solar radiation hits the earth, and supplies it with the energy which produces weather phenomena, and permits life to exist on our planet.

The heat rays in the solar radiation keep the water of the oceans liquid (except in the polar regions), and set into operation the cycle of water: from the seas into the clouds, into rains, into rivers, and back into the seas.

The visible part of the solar spectrum, with shorter waves than those of the heat radiation (which mainly accounts for the evaporation of water from the oceans), is absorbed by plants, and utilized by them for the formation of organic matter through photosynthesis. This is a complicated photochemical process: a reorganization of the electronic clouds of certain atoms and atomic groups under the influence of light. The amount of energy involved in such a transformation of a single atom or atomic group, is extremely small compared to that liberated in a single fusion process in the interior of the sun. By passing through the sun and spreading into space the energy has been "devalued." Yet it is this devalued chemical energy stored by plants that supports all life on earth; mankind has been satisfied with its use until our time.

The energy resources of man in the first period of his history, which can be called the natural state, consisted of his own muscular power and of that of his domesticated animals. A small additional amount could be derived from the meteorological cycle: water mills and windmills for work, sailing ships for transportation. From the point of view of science, the natural energy of man—his muscular power—is the least understood of all. It represents a conversion of chemical energy (liberated through a change in the configuration of electronic clouds in certain atomic groups) into gross mechanical energy, with marked increase in temperature. In the laboratory we are familiar with processes of this type only in primitive pieces of apparatus, such as electric batteries. What takes place in organisms is immensely complicated and refined.

In a natural state, man lives from his energy income, not from capital. This income (solar radiation) is available everywhere, although not quite uniformly distributed over the different climatic zones.

Because of the universality of every resource in natural state of life on earth, specific local conditions have been of relatively little imporance for the course of history: other factors—above all, geography, national character, and personality—have played the decisive role. This is why, in the usual presentations of history, the energy supply has been taken for granted, and interest concentrated on entirely different factors. This was justified as long as the natural state of mankind persisted; but it is incorrect—and dangerous—to continue this approach into our time. Violent changes have taken place, and their importance is not properly accounted for if they are described merely in an addendum to the chapter dealing with the economic or cultural developments.

As for Europe, in this first natural period of history it did not play any special role that would distinguish it from other continents: it had its wars and peace treaties, its kings and its heroes, its constitutions and revolutions, philosophies, religions, arts and sciences, and all else that goes with them. Only one phenomenon had lifted Europe, by that time, out of the chaotic stream of human events: the emergence of the Greek man. He originated free, independent thinking, aimed at exploring the nature of the world, without regard to immediate practical use. From this spring came profound, new discoveries in mathematics and natural science. These discoveries were buried in subsequent centuries, but were uncovered again thousands of years later, when the true flowering of Europe began.

Then came the second chapter in the era of chemistry. Black powder supposedly was discovered in China, but it seems to have been used there mainly for the gay spectacle of fireworks. When it appeared in Europe in the twelfth or thirteenth century, it immediately became a weapon.

I place this event at the beginning of the second phase of the chemical age because it represented the first utilization of chemical energy accumulated outside the living muscle. To me, it is symbolic of the European spirit, as it was to reveal itself from then on, with its most characteristic attributes: ingenuity of mind, inventive power, lust for adventure, and drive for expansion, stopping at nothing, despite—yes, often in the name of—Christianity.

It was a time of transition, a violent development. It is impossible to keep its spiritual aspects apart from the material ones, because, without overcoming religious and philosophical traditions, the amazing blossoming out of research in natural sciences, witnessed in these centuries, would not have been feasible; inversely, the success of scientific research contributed much to the break with the traditional dogmas.

The great exploratory voyages of this time made the spherical shape of the earth a reality; Europeans with their cannons became masters of a large part of the globe. They considered themselves masters of the universe, since they believed that the earth was its center. Copernicus destroyed this exalted standing and made the earth one planet among many. This, however, did not greatly detract from the pride of European man; he found compensation for his former position of ascendancy in the universe in the possession of science that had solved the mysteries of the sky and was about to solve the mysteries of nature on earth. From the study of the motion of planets, the science of mechanics grew. This in turn gave physics a powerful impulse. From the medieval mysticism of alchemy there arose the precise science of chemistry. At the end of the eighteenth century, the transition was completed, and the steam engine made its appearance.

The steam engine was from its beginning coupled with coal, a fuel which came into use in England after the destruction of the old forests. The first steam engines were used for pumping water out of coal pits. They consumed coal and more coal. In other words, they used up the capital energy which the sun had accumulated on earth in hundreds of millions of years through the growth of forests, which then sank into the ground and were carbonized. The production of mechanical energy began to mount upward, and this changed the whole life of Western European man. Sociologists speak of *industrial* revolution; but this term neglects the main thing: it was an *energetic* revolution; the rest was a mere consequence. The working-man, who until then had at his disposal nothing but his "manpower," was now provided with an increasing quantity of "horsepower." This quantity keeps changing from year to year and is widely different in different countries. It is by far the highest in the United States, where today an average worker commands about forty horsepower. Increased production and rise of the living standard follow this increase in power available to every man.

True, at first the new wealth flowed mainly into the pockets of a few entrepreneurs, while the situation of the masses became worse. The passage of long years and many political revolutions were needed before general well-being began to grow. It is not my task to survey these social transformations, but I would like to emphasize here certain characteristics of this period.

The first concerns the mutual interaction of technology and science. The steam engine was invented before the theory of the process on which this engine is based became known. The very concept of energy, which now is our key to the understanding of the steam engine (the concept on which I am trying to base here a summary of all human history), first arose only about fifty years later, when the so-called mechanical heat theory was developed. Since that time, however, the concept of energy (together with the more sophisticated concept of entropy) has contributed essentially to the improvement of the steam engine. Similar interplay between technology and science has gradually spread into all branches of research and industry.

In the second place, I would like to mention here two most important examples of the interrelation of science and technology—electricity and chemistry. Through electrotechnics, energy first became easily transportable—a commerical product. Chemistry freed man from his dependence on natural materials. It is impossible to list here the other new things which made their appearance in the same period. When I was young even bicycles were not yet in general use. Today we have airplanes with supersonic speed. What always astonishes me when I think of it is that the whole technological age is hardly twice as old as I am myself; and by far the most amazing wonders of this age have come forth in the second half, which I have witnessed. Most astonishing are perhaps the triumphs of medicine; for example, in doubling the average life expectancy of man.

My third point concerns the liquid fuel, oil. Large quantities of it are extracted from the ground, and it has become an important factor in economic and political power struggles. However, even if these natural resources did not exist, the number of automobiles and planes probably would have been not much smaller than it is now, because man has learned (a generation ago) how to make liquid fuel from coal.

Truly it has been a fantastic time, these last one hundred fifty years. Is it not evident that a given supply of things must have an end, if it is continuously used, and that the end will come quicker the faster the use? The Europeans—including the Russians and European descendants in America—have, however, lived just that way, day by day, without regard to the more distant future. They solidified and extended their mastery over other nations, acquired at an earlier time with the help of the cannon. After the Napoleonic Wars they were, for a while, so deeply engaged in this expansion that they kept peace between themselves. The middle of the nineteenth century was one of the longest peaceful periods in Europe. Later, however, European nations again began fighting among themselves partly for the loot of their colonial expansion, and partly over the old, unsettled power conflicts and territorial disputes in Europe. Meanwhile, the military establishment itself became gradually mechanized and industrialized, like every other branch of life. The terrors of war rose correspondingly, and the result we have all seen came to pass: the two world wars, which devastated Europe and deprived it of its leading role in world politics—even if some European nations are not quite aware of it yet. The two great powers of today, the United States and the Soviet Union, continue the old disastrous game of power politics, still more exacerbated by an ideological conflict—here liberal capitalism, there totalitarian communism—a struggle reminiscent of religious controversies of earlier centuries in the fanatic belief of each of the two parties that complete justice is on its side.

To me, a fundamental characteristic of the age the end of which we are now witnessing has been the unconcern with which men have used up the very source of their wealth and power: the fossil fuels, coal and oil. The immense upswing of living conditions following the utilization of these sources of energy engendered an optimism, a firm belief in progress, which would admit of no limits. This belief suffered a heavy blow in Europe through the two great wars, but survived in America and Russia. And yet, such trust in the future was quite unjustified until recently. Coal and oil had to give out sooner or later, and the sooner the greater number of people on earth. The advances of medicine and hygiene ensured the growth of mankind in Europe, America, and Australia. More and more people of other continents—above all, the immense human masses of China and India—began to yearn for a higher standard of living, and started to

Europe and Science

industrialize themselves. New coal and oil deposits were continuously discovered; there was no need to worry about the next decades, perhaps even about the next few centuries.

For the scientist, however, today's civilization is merely a small interval in the long existence of the human race—a total of perhaps a half million years; and the latter period itself appears to be only a minute interval in the endless eons of the development of life on earth. He has the right to use a larger time scale, and to decide that until a short while ago the hope of mankind to sustain its domination over the globe rested on very weak foundations.

To substantiate this conviction one has only to remember the great physicist Lord Rutherford, the discoverer of the nucleus and the father of today's nuclear physics, who at the time of his death in 1937 believed that it would be forever impossible to put to practical use the immense energies stored in the atomic nuclei. He was wrong. Just two years after Rutherford's death, one of his pupils (who, like Rutherford, has dedicated his life to the pursuit of pure science in the Greek spirit), the German chemist Otto Hahn, carried out—together with his co-worker, Strassmann—a crucial experiment, without suspecting its consequences. Probably many years would have passed before Hahn's discovery became ripe for technical utilization, if it were not for the Second World War, which accelerated the research processes just as a catalyst accelerates a chemical reaction.

We deal here not with the fusion of light nuclei, which keeps the sun going, but with the breakdown, or "fission," of heavy nuclei. In principle, this process is easy to understand. I said before that electrical forces cannot explain the association of nucleons in the nucleus: first, because all protons have positive charges and therefore repel each other; and second, because electrical forces do not act on neutrons. I related how Yukawa concluded from the fundamental principles of modern physics, that a new kind of force must exist between the nucleons, and associated them with a new kind of elementary particle, the meson. The Yukawa forces act only among nearest neighbors, while electrical repulsions act over larger distances. It is understandable that as the nuclei become larger, the electrical repulsion—despite its relative weakness—ultimately must exceed the short-range attraction. Therefore, nuclei above a certain size are unstable. This instability first occurs in the element uranium, which contains 92 protons. It was found that one of the isotopes of this element—not the most common one, with 146 neutrons, but the considerably rarer one with 143 neutrons—becomes unstable when it takes one more neutron from the outside, and breaks into two approximately equal parts with the release of an immense amount of energy. A few free neutrons are also emitted in this process, and these in turn can associate with the unstable uranium isotope, and cause the fission of more nuclei. A chain reaction, reminiscent of an avalanche, is the result. This is the process used to liberate energy in uranium reactors; it is also the basis of the first atom bomb.

The fundamental steps in this development—the discovery of nuclear fission itself, its theoretical interpretation, and the realization of the possibility of a chain reaction, took place in Europe, or were made by European scientists newly arrived in the United States. On the other hand, the applied technological development—an immense achievement of will power and organization—was American. The tragedy of this development was that the first use made of the new forces was in a military weapon of unimaginable destructive power.

The production of energy from nuclear fission got under way soon after the end of the war; today uranium reactors are operating in several countries, and many more are under construction.

Like coal and oil, the raw materials from which this energy is derived, uranium and thorium, exist on earth only in finite amounts, but these are large enough to postpone the catastrophe of energy starvation by centuries.

Among all industrialized nations the one in which the steam engine was discovered, England, was the one most threatened by approaching exhaustion of coal supplies. Today it is leading in the development of uranium reactors and sees in them its hope for the preservation of its industrial position in the world. Many countries which have no coal or oil, and therefore little or no industry, believe that they will be able to build their industry up on the basis of uranium power stations. And already, the next step is in sight, which promises to make available inexhaustible amounts of nuclear "fuel."

It has proved possible to realize on earth the fusion process which supplies the energy of stars—the synthesis of helium nuclei from four nucleons. A uranium fission bomb had to be used to initiate the process. The immense temperatures and pressures created by the fission explosion brought the fusion process under way. As in the case of black powder and of the uranium bomb, here, too, a technical breakthrough was due to war—or at least, to preparations for war. The history of the hydrogen bomb is well known and does not need to be retold. It is now a decisive factor in the power struggle between the United States and the

Soviet Union. Europe took no part in it until recently, when Great Britain took up the manufacture of H-bombs. At first this seemed an entirely diabolical invention, since there was no way in sight to slow down the process of fusion. To make use of it as a source of industrial power, however, in a remarkably short time, methods were found which now make it probable that the so-called thermonuclear processes also will be brought under control in the near future. When this is achieved, mankind will be rid of all concern about its energy supply, for a period to be reckoned not in centuries but in geological eras, because the raw material for fusion is an isotope of hydrogen, which can be obtained from the water of the oceans—and oceans will be there at least as long as the human race survives. This then looks like a return to a sound state of human affairs. Man will be able to live from a reserve of cosmic energy practically as inexhaustible as the energy of the sun.

Three fundamental characteristics distinguish this new state from the first, natural period of human history. In the first place, it will be an artificial state, which can be sustained only by continuous employment of the most refined technical methods, and only on the basis of international cooperation.

In the second place, if the available means are properly used, it will be a state of great material wealth. The energy available to a worker will not be the small amount which his muscles can derive from his food, but the unlimited quantity which human intelligence can conjure through research, technology, and organization.

Finally, it will be a very unstable state, fraught with dangers of an entirely different order of magnitude from those which confronted mankind in the pretechnological time. Political upheavals, wars, and revolutions of earlier times damaged or destroyed limited areas. A political catastrophe in the new era will mean self-annihilation of our civilization, perhaps even of all mankind, if not of all life on earth.

Let us summarize: Through the spirit and the labor of Europe, mankind has made itself independent of the scanty income of solar energy allotted to it by nature. The European man first discovered the reserves of solar energy, stored in past eras in fossil fuels; tempted by the promise of treasures to gain, he has squandered these reserves thoughtlessly to build up a new industrial civilization, gradually extended over the whole of the earth. However, he has not quite forgotten the spirit of Greek civilization, which gave the initial impulse to this development: in his pursuit of material wealth, he has continued to cultivate research for its own sake. From this pure research, came man's release from the danger of ultimate extinction through exhaustion of fossil fuels; nuclear energy, stored in the earth itself, was put to man's use.

However, like Prometheus, who had to expiate his deed of robbing the gods of fire and bringing it to man, so modern man, who has started the cosmic fire on earth, is burdened by a curse. He has opened the atomic age by frightful destruction and mass murder, and there will forever remain visible the shadow cast over the joy and hope of life by the words "atom bomb."

Scientists were the ones who brought man to this crossroads. It is now up to all men—without exception, not only the political leaders—to avoid the road to catastrophe. We, the physicists, must keep explaining and warning; we must seek to gain influence on the decisions of statesmen. This was my purpose in trying to present here world history, and Europe's role in it, from the point of view of a scientist. The great danger for the future are men who refuse to admit that the new age, upon whose threshold we now stand, is fundamentally different from all past ages. I have already spoken of its three characteristics. The first one, the technical effort needed for its perpetuation, is a burden. The third, the atomic bomb, is a terrible danger.

The question arises: is it not possible to have the prosperity without the burden and the danger—or, at least, if the burden is unavoidable, without the danger? One tragic aspect of the situation is that with a slightly different sequence of historical accidents this could perhaps have been possible. Through advances in physics and technology, mankind could have continued living prosperously on solar energy, without touching the nuclear energy of the earth. True, the power of falling water, which is what comes to mind first in this connection, would not suffice. Even full utilization of all possible hydroelectric systems on earth would have covered only a small percentage of the energy requirements of mankind. Winds are too unreliable. The utilization of tides is under study, and promises a not negligible contribution. A serious possibility is direct conversion of solar energy into electricity through so-called thermoelements. I can give you a few figures, taken from a paper by the Russian physicist Joffe.* In a single day, the solar energy reaching the earth is equal to the sum of all energy which has been stored, since the beginnings of the earth, in the form of coal, oil, or water. This shows that the energy paucity, characteristic of the era I have called the "natural period" of history, was due not to limited supply of solar energy, but to the very low efficiency with which this supply is utilized in the me-

* A. Joffe, *Le Journal de Physique et de Radium*, 18 (April 1957), 14.

teorological cycle and in the growth of plants. Today the efficiency of improved thermoelements reaches 8-10 per cent, which is comparable with the efficiency of small steam engines. Of course, to cover the world requirements of energy by means of such devices would require that a large area of desert, with year-round exposure to the sun—something like fifty by fifty kilometers—be covered with thermoelectric elements.

Even if it proves possible to carry out such projects in the future, this cannot change the tragic situation into which the bombs of Hiroshima and Nagasaki have led us. War and violence have stood as godfathers at the cradle of the new era. We have used the gift of providence for murder and destruction. The curse of this deed will be always upon us.

This crisis cannot be resolved by traditional political means. We hear people say: When the longbow was invented, or black powder was discovered, prophets predicted the end of the world, but mankind has survived this and many other things, too—dynamite, aerial bombs, napalm. In the same way, mankind—or at least a part of it—will survive also A- and H-bombs, if only the necessary protective measures are carried out, such as by burying ourselves in subterranean cities, or by other means. To me, people who speak like this seem foolish. We are not moles. We enjoy life in the sun, and the glorious landscape around us. Without changing our thinking radically, no way out of the present danger can be found. The difficulties are overwhelming, since seldom has the world been in such an upheaval as it is now. The nations of Asia and Africa strive to get rid of colonial rule, and of the influence of Europe. The struggle of conflicting nationalisms, religious antagonisms, racial tensions, competing ideologies—such as totalitarian communism and liberal capitalism—is fiercer now than ever; and yet it is not possible to settle these controversies by the old violent means. A new world war would mean the end of us all.

Europe started all this, through its discoveries and inventions. These have been products of the brain, directed at material advancement. I believe that Europe must once again take over the leadership—but this time, in the field of ethical and political progress. The first step in this direction would be Europe's own unity.

As a physicist, I am particularly interested in European institutions which have directly to do with atomic research, such as Euratom and CERN. The laboratories of the latter lie before the gates of Geneva. The dimensions of the machines installed there demonstrate that the smallest particles of nature yield the greatest energies, and that their study therefore requires the greatest experimental efforts and expenditures. It is a gratifying sign of the solidarity of Western European nations, that they did get together in this undertaking, which exceeded the capacities of every one of them separately.

Physics is not only a source of material progress, it is also a link in the chain of spiritual development of man. Ultimately, the conflict between East and West, which now keeps the world in turmoil, is due to different philosophical concepts and interpretations of life, which can be traced to the influence of natural science. Eastern Marxism teaches that communist economy is a historical necessity, and from this conviction stems its fanaticism. Yet, this idea is the descendant of physical determinism, which grew from Newton's mechanics of cosmic bodies; physics turned away from this deterministic philosophy thirty years ago. Physics has now developed the statistical interpretation of the laws of nature, which corresponds better to reality; from this new viewpoint, the belief of the communists in the inevitable realization of Marxist predictions seems grotesque. American thinking, on the other hand, is deep in the grip of a superficial pragmatism, which identifies truth with usefulness. This belief I cannot share. I believe, for example, that the laws of nuclear physics have a high content of truth; but whether their discovery will bring human society ultimate boon, or only death and destruction, can only be revealed by the future.

Europe is not committed to either of these two extreme and, I believe, absurd doctrines. We believe that there must be a reasonable middle way, that it is madness to gamble with the existence of civilized mankind, in order to assure victory of a philosophical doctrine or an economic system. I, for one, believe that mass murder and war are evil under all circumstances, and that in the future politics must get along without them. However, it has been arrogant enough of me to consider historical problems through the eyes of a physicist. It would mean going still further beyond my field of competence if I were to enlarge now on moral philosophy, not to speak of theology. Let me only say in conclusion that the ethical problems which have arisen from the enormous increase in power available to man are perhaps even closer to my heart than the scientific and political ones; and that I hope that more will be heard on this theme from men more competent than I.

FOUR

Blessings and Evils of Space Travel

The space-travel enthusiast who reads the title of this chapter might think, Behold! This implacable enemy of space travel is already so far converted that while he preaches its evils he also grasps its possible blessings. I must ask him not to crow too soon. I certainly want to assemble all that can be said in favor of cosmic adventures, but then I want to evaluate it and draw my conclusions.

If you want to form a judgment on the value of space travel, you must start with the question: value for whom? Many branches of science are involved, such as astronomy, physics, geophysics, meteorology, cosmology, biologic evolution, and others. All these are intent upon learning something about outer space and the bodies that move in it—not only about the moon, the planets, and the fixed stars, but also about the countless atomic particles of the most varied sort. Apart from the scientists, many sorts of technicians, researchers in the field of materials and propulsion, rocket builders, electronics specialists, and others, and the industries they serve want to learn, less for the sake of knowledge in itself than for its applications and, naturally, to earn money. Add to these all the inventors and users of the communications media who span the oceans with the help of artificial satellites and thus make possible television broadcasts from continent to continent. And finally there are the military who see the space probes as research devices for their nuclear bomb carriers and who hope that they can soon include outer space in their strategic plans.

Is that not enough? Surely I have forgotten many important things—I am indeed no space-travel expert. Can we not be happy and proud about all this? Certainly all those specialists and interested parties can. But where are we, you and I? Allow me to start, contrary to the rules of etiquette, with myself. I am a physicist and I am interested in those results of space research that relate to the physics of the atmosphere, to the radiation belt around the earth, to cosmic rays, to meteors. Previously the laws of planetary motion, which Newton elucidated almost three hundred years ago, could only be checked by observation of the orbits of the natural heavenly bodies. These laws have now been confirmed by direct experiment with bodies created by man, and that is an intellectual pleasure for me. It is to be expected that in the near future Einstein's relativistic mechanics, which today replace Newton's classical mechanics, will be checked by experiment with artificial satellites. That would give me even greater delight.

But then how many men share these pleasures? Can they justify our exertions for space travel? Only someone who is so absorbed in his specialty that he forgets all other points of view can think so. Experimenting costs money, and the further the investigation progresses, the higher are the costs. But the outlay must stand in reasonable ratio to the results, and this is not so with space research. The results are of considerable interest for the specialists, but it is just these scientifically interesting results that leave the layman cold.

How many of you would share my pleasure in the proof of classical and relativistic mechanics which I have just mentioned? How many are impressed by the discovery of the Van Allen belt? By the meteor counts? By the measurement of cosmic radiation outside our atmosphere? Who has even a clear concept of the dimensions of the universe? Everyone knows they are measured by the astronomers in "light years"—a poorly chosen term, for it signifies not a time but a distance:

it is the distance that light traverses in a year. Light travels 186,000 miles per second. The nearest fixed star is about four light years away; the most distant visible objects, many billions of light years away. But the distance to the moon is about a light second—less than one thirty-millionth of a light year. Thus, when we succeed in landing on the moon, it will be only this tiniest fraction of the distance to the nearest fixed star that has been reached.

A moon landing would indeed be a daring and splendid technical and organizational achievement. But is it really a voyage into space? It could be regarded perhaps as a thrust into the planetary system. Is this a worthwhile goal? We know that none of the other planets is sufficiently like our earth to make human life possible on them. They are ice cold, or glowing hot balls, without water and air, and completely unsuited for immigration. Travel to the fixed stars, some of which may well have an inhabitable planet, is today still a fantastic dream. There are of course rocket specialists who study the technological problems of the project—for instance, propelling devices that use radiation pressure—or ponder the problem of the immensely long travel time. For this purpose, a result of Einstein's relativity theory is used, according to which a traveler who is moving at high velocity —close to that of light—ages more slowly than his twin brother who remains at home. These considerations, which are well established theoretically and experimentally, throw the glamour of scientific method over speculations about space travel. But they do not bring us back into the domain of rationality.

In February 1958, I said (at a discussion held at the Evangelical Academy in Kloster Loccum) that space travel is a triumph of intellect but a tragic failure of reason, and this sentence has often been quoted. In the journal *Christ und Welt,* April 1960, these words were again quoted, with the addition: "I am quite clear that my remarks will not stop these things, and *that they are not to be stopped.*" Actually I did not say, "that they are not to be stopped." If I had, I would have been denying my sense of responsibility which prohibits me from being fascinated by technical gadgets to such a degree that I lose the perspective of the sciences in the frame of human culture as a whole.

In a television program, "The Voyage into the Dark," in June 1961, I supplemented this idea with the words: "Intellect distinguishes between the possible and the impossible; reason distinguishes between the sensible and the senseless. Even the possible can be senseless." This was interpreted to signify that I considered the existence of the human race as senseless. I am no such pessimist. I believe that humanity, once alerted, will shake on the reign of technology and the boast of being all-powerful, and will return to real values, sensible and necessary: to peace, to human love, to humility, to reverence, to contentedness, to high art, and to true science. The present so-called space travel seems to me not to be true science. Even the name is a deception. The thing has nothing to do with the immense spaces of the universe. It is a matter of supra-atmosphere circling of the earth and of thrusts to the moon and the nearest planets; in short, an investigation of the neighborhood of the earth.

There are leading astronomers and physicists who today show no great enthusiasm for "astronautics." In the British satirical magazine *Punch*, an article appeared not long ago in which were collected statements by astronomers concerning space travel dating from the first sputnik up to the present day. There it can be seen how the evaluation of space travel for scientific ends has changed from initial agreement to the sharpest rejection. The well-known Cambridge astronomer Fred Hoyle has said: "The Soviet-American space race is almost worthless for scientific research. What has been accomplished is not worth a thousandth part of what has been spent." And the British physicist and Nobel Prize winner Sir John Cockcroft said: "We smile as we watch your space flights on television. Your efforts represent a distortion of science in the name of competition with the Soviet Union."

What motivates the average citizen to sacrifice a not inconsiderable portion of his taxes for space travel is surely not scientific interest. But what is it? Perhaps the possibility of practical uses—for example, improvement of weather predictions, or the enlargement of the transmission range of television with the help of artificial satellites? I do not believe that ordinary people are swayed by such motives. Who cares how the meteorologists come to their conclusions? Who is burning to see "live" on the television screen some chief of state in Asia or Africa, instead of seeing him in a few days in the newsreels? But the individual citizen has little choice.

There are, however, huge sectors of public life that expect to profit from the development of planet and space research. Let us look and see how many blessings are hiding here. One of these sectors is industry. The construction of rockets places enormous demands on the perfection of materials and on the precision of the work. It forces us, therefore, to new technological progress. This is particularly true in the areas of electronics automation, of the chemistry of fuels and explosives, and of metallurgy. There is the claim that a country which does not take part in space travel will remain behind in all these areas, and will not be capable of competition. Against this stands the fact that the technique of space travel absorbs a high percentage of available brain power and withdraws it from other purposes. It is questionable whether the damage thus inflicted upon the overall economy is balanced by the benefits. A pure blessing seems not to be hiding here.

Another sector of public life which derives benefits from space travel is the military. They continually demand more perfect rockets for the delivery of atomic bombs. Space travel is obviously a splendid means to reach this goal in scientific disguise. Only under such a cloak can those monstrous expenditures be made available for space research. After the goal of intercontinental ballistic missiles was reached, the use of artificial satellites for the purpose of espionage and of bomb dropping was considered, and the resources continued to flow. Today the practicability of these weapons of war is in doubt, because stationary satellites circling the earth are more vulnerable than guided missiles. However that might be, apart from military specialists and politicians, no one is likely to consider these applications of space travel as a source of blessings. War has never belonged to the domain of reason, and today it is pure madness.

So we come to the conclusion that scientific and practical considerations can explain easily the interest in space research of groups of specialists, but not that of mankind in general. Yet without doubt, such an interest exists. What are its roots? Mankind is fascinated by the splendor of the undertaking, the enormous cost, the complication, the complexity and the size of the apparatus, the expenditure in men, machinery, materials; still more, there is the romance of the drive into the unknown, the uncertain. In addition there is the old longing of mankind to release itself from Mother Earth and to reach for the stars. Add to this the admiration for the clever and tough engineer who figures all this out and brings it about—and for the heroes of the show, the space pilots. Even those who know that these men are not heroes like Achilles or Siegfried, but a smoothly fitting part of an apparatus thought out and steered by others, cannot help but admire their bravery. These motives all appeal to our highest ideals. They are used by the specialists of science, technology, industry, politics, and war in order to further their special interests, to make their plans popular, and to get more money out of the taxpayers.

So I am unable to see any blessing in space travel as it is pursued today in the United States, the Soviet Union, and in other countries. It would be different if it were a common undertaking of all peoples which would act for the reconciliation of antagonisms and the maintenance of peace. But that is exactly what it does not do. It is a symbol of a contest between the great powers, a weapon in the cold war, an emblem of national vanity, a demonstration of power. In addition, I do not believe in the frequently stated opinion that space travel would be a lightning conductor for our inborn aggressiveness and violence, which otherwise discharge themselves in wars. For it is used directly as a preparation for war, a dangerous game. There is no guarantee that, for example, in the competition to reach the moon, the fairness customary in sport will be retained. Who assures us that the party who wins in that contest will not succumb to the madness of believing that he possesses absolute superiority, and will not seek to exploit the moment in order to win mastery over the earth? So long as the projects of space travel are still bound up with the image of national greatness and power, so long as the public at large is deceived over their scientific and practical possibilities, that long will I be unable to discover any blessing in it in spite of all my admiration of the accomplishment.

FIVE

Symbol and Reality

If someone who is no physicist, chemist, or astronomer were to glance through any book on these sciences, he would be struck by the amount of mathematical and other symbols and the scarcity of descriptions of natural phenomena. Even the instruments of observation are indicated only symbolically by diagrams. And yet these books claim to deal with natural science. Where in this accumulation of formulae is living nature? How are the physical and chemical symbols connected with the experienced reality of sense perceptions?

Even the scientist himself will occasionally ponder over the reasons why he approaches nature in this abstract and formalistic way by means of symbols. The opinion is often expressed that the symbols are just a matter of convenience, a kind of shorthand needed to handle and to master the abundance of the material. Yet I think the problem is deeper. I have considered this question in detail and have convinced myself that the symbols are an essential part of the method for penetrating into the physical reality behind phenomena. I shall try to explain this idea in this way:

To a simple, unlearned person, reality is what he feels and perceives. The real existence of the things surrounding him seems to be just as certain as the sensations of pain, joy, or hope that he feels. He is perhaps shown an optical illusion which reveals to him that a perception may lead to doubtful or even utterly incorrect judgments about actual facts. But this always remains on the surface of consciousness, a curious, amusing exception.

This attitude is called naïve realism. The great majority of people maintain this disposition of mind throughout their lives, even if they learn to distinguish between subjective experience, like pleasure, pain, expectation, disappointment, and objective experiences which have to do with things of the external world.

But there are people to whom something happens which stirs them deeply and makes them skeptical. This is what happened in my case.

I had an elder cousin who was a university student while I was still at school. Apart from lectures on chemistry, he attended a course in philosophy which impressed him. Once he asked me suddenly: "What do you mean exactly when you call this leaf, here, green or the sky, there, blue?" I regarded this question as rather superfluous and answered: "I just mean green and blue because I see it like that, exactly as you see it." But this did not satisfy him. "How do you know that I see green exactly as you see it?" My answer, "Because all people see it in the same way, of course," still did not satisfy him: "There are color-blind people who see the colors differently; some of them, for example, cannot distinguish red and green." Thus he drove me in a corner and made it plain to me that there is no way to ascertain what another person perceives and that even the statement "He perceives the same as I" has no clear meaning.

Thus it dawned upon me that fundamentally everything is subjective, everything without exception. That was a shock.

The problem was not to distinguish the subjective from the objective, but to understand how to free one-self from the subjective and to arrive at objective statements. I want to say right from the beginning that I have found no satisfactory answer to this in any philosophical treatise. But through my occupation with physics and its allied sciences I have arrived, near the end of my life, at a solution which appears to me to some extent acceptable.

Long ago, as a young fellow, I followed the advice of my cousin and mentor who told me to read Kant. Later on I learned that the problem of how objective knowledge arises from the sense perceptions of the individual and what this knowledge means is a much older one; that, for example, Plato's doctrine of ideas is an early formulation, followed by various speculations of antique and medieval philosophers up to Kant's immediate precursors, the British empiricists Locke, Berkeley, and Hume. However, I do not intend to speak about the history of philosophy; I only want to say a few words about Kant because he has influenced the thought of men up to our time, and because I intend to use some of his terminology.

I quote a passage from Kant's *Critique of Pure Reason* (Transcendental Aesthetics): "Objects are given us by way of sense impressions, they produce our perceptions. They are then taken up by reason, which produces concepts." Thus Kant suggests that the objects of perception are transformed by reason into concepts. He takes it as self-evident that the objects of perception are the same for all individuals and that the concepts formed by reason are molded alike by all individuals. According to Kant, all knowledge refers to the phenomena but is not determined solely by experience (a posteriori) but also by the structure of our reason (a priori). The a priori forms of our perception are space and time; the a priori forms of reason are called categories; Kant gives a catalogue of these which contains, for example, causality.

The question whether behind the world of phenomena there is another world of objects in their own right (noumena) is, as far as I understand, left unanswered by Kant. He speaks about the "thing in itself" but declares it as unknowable. I quote a passage from Bertrand Russell's book *Wisdom of the West* (London: Macdonald, 1957); he says on page 241:

> On the Kantian theory it is impossible to experience a thing in itself, since all experience occurs with the concurrence of space, time and the categories. We may at best infer that there are such things from the postulated external source of impressions. Strictly speaking, even that is not permissible, since we have no independent way of finding out that there are such sources, and even if we had, we could still not say that they were causing our sense impressions. For if we speak of causality we are already inside the network of a priori concepts operating within the understanding.

The vague concept of the "thing in itself" is generally considered a weak point of Kant's teaching. One has to assume something like that in order to understand how the sense perceptions and their conceptual elaborations of the single individuals can lead to objective statements valid for all individuals. But this precondition of all objective knowledge is declared by Kant to be itself unknowable.

I shall try to show how one can escape this dilemma by using scientific methods of thinking. But first I wish to give a short survey of the attitude to this problem taken by philosophical systems after Kant.

I cannot dwell on the prehistory of the problem of how subjective experiences were transformed into objective knowledge but only remark that it has already been vaguely discussed by Plato in his well-known simile of the cave, and more thoroughly by later philosophers, in particular by the skeptic thinker David Hume. The philosophers after Kant have taken very different attitudes to it.

There are some philosophical systems which admit as real only the world of the single individual, the ipse. In my youth a German book by Stirner, *The Individual and His Property*, was widely read; as the title reveals it takes this "solipsistic" standpoint. The fact that I remember the title of the book shows that I was impressed by it.

Much more widely accepted is the opinion, apparently shared by Kant, that it is self-evident and needs no demonstration, that the sense perceptions of different individuals are identical and that the question is only to investigate this common world of phenomena. This view is taken by the so-called "idealistic systems" which culminated in Hegel, and of several others, among them the "phenomenology" of Husserl, whose lectures I attended sixty years ago in Göttingen. He taught that one could obtain knowledge by a process of the mind called "basic contemplation" (*Wesenchau*). But that did not satisfy me.

The school of logical positivism which has its roots in the work of the physicist and philosopher Ernst Mach and is today widely accepted teaches a doctrine less obscure but still more radical. Only the immediate sense impressions are regarded as real; everything else, the whole conceptual world of everyday life and of science, is considered to have no other purpose than to constitute logical connections between the sense impressions. The American philosopher Margenau has introduced the term "constructs" for all that. In the most radical interpretation this theory means a denial of the existence of an external world, or at least the negation of its knowability. In practical life a follower of this doctrine would hardly behave as if there were no external world. All these theories are relying on the same assumption that the world of sensual perception is "the same" for all individuals. What this means is left open.

The "materialism" of the communistic bloc of Eastern nations calls all these theories "idealistic" and opposes them violently. It maintains, of course without proof, just as an axiom, the existence of a reality independent of the subject. Marx and Engels seem to have regarded this like the naïve realist: matter is primary, consciousness of mind is one of its manifestations. This "mechanical materialism," however, was not easily reconciled with the results of progressing physics. For here the primitive ideas about matter were dissolved and replaced by the concept of "field" and eventually by still more abstract ideas. Therefore Lenin invented the "dialectical materialism" wherein the old term "matter" is preserved but understood in such a general way that nothing of its meaning is preserved (just as it happened with his use of other words such as "democracy"). The fundamental axiom is "the existence of a real, objectively knowable external world." Since in the East Lenin's philosophy has become a kind of official religion, a problem which has occupied and worried the minds of so many thinkers has now become an article of faith guarded by the power of the State.

Now what is the opinion of the physicists, or, more general, of the scientists about the problem of reality?

I should think that most of them are naïve realists who do not rack their brains about philosophical subtleties. They are content to observe a phenomenon, to measure it and describe it in their characteristic jargon. As long as they have to do with instruments and experimental paraphernalia they use ordinary language adorned with suitable technical terms, as in every craft.

But as soon as they begin to theorize, that is, to interprete their observations, they use another means of communication. Already in Newtonian mechanics, the first physical theory in the modern sense of the term, there appear concepts which do not correspond to ordinary things, like force, mass, energy. With the progress of research this tendency became more and more pronounced. In Maxwell's theory of electromagnetism the concept of the field was developed which is quite outside the world of perceptible things. Quantitative laws expressed by mathematical formulae, like Maxwell's equations, became more and more prevalent. This happened in the theory of relativity, in atomic physics, in modern chemistry. Eventually we had in quantum mechanics an instance wherein the mathematical formalism was developed rather completely and successfully before an interpretation in ordinary language was found, and even today this is not finally fixed.

What is going on here? In physics the mathematical formulae are not an end in themselves, as in pure mathematics, but symbols for some kind of reality which lies beyond the level of everyday experiences.

I maintain that this fact is closely connected with the question: how is it possible to obtain from subjective experiences objective knowledge?

I propose to approach this problem with the methods of thinking used by the physicist. Only a minor part of these methods is derived from philosophical systems. They have just been developed because the traditional thinking of philosophers has failed when applied to modern physics. Their strength lies in the fact that they have been successful. I mean not only that they have contributed to the understanding of natural phenomena but that they have led to the discovery of new, often overwhelmingly impressive phenomena, and to human domination over nature.

The consideration which I suggest does not, however, come under the title of "empiricism" which the metaphysicists regard with contempt. The rules of thought used by the physicist are not derived from experience, but are pure ideas, inventions of great thinkers. However, they are tested on an extremely large field of experience. Hence I intend not to deal with philosophy of science, but to look at philosophy from the scientific standpoint. I am sure that the metaphysicists will object to it. But I cannot help it.

To begin with I shall enumerate some of these methods of thinking and discuss their origin and their successes.

I suggest the expression "decidability" for a fundamental rule of scientific thinking (although I did not find the word in the dictionary): use a concept only if it is decidable, whether it can be applied in a special case or not.

When in electrodynamics and optics of moving bodies apparently unsurmountable difficulties were met, Einstein discovered that these can be reduced to the assumption that the concept of simultaneity of events at the different places has an absolute significance. This he showed is not the case, due to the fact that the velocity of light used for signaling is finite; with the help of physical means one can only establish relative simultaneity with respect to a definite coordinate (inertial) system. The idea led to the special theory of relativity and to a new doctrine of space and time. Kant's ideas of space and time as a priori forms of intuition were thus finally refuted.

Actually doubts about this had risen much earlier. A short time after Kant, non-Euclidean geometries had been discovered (by Gauss, Bolyai, Lobatschefski) as logical possibilities. Gauss made an attempt to decide experimentally whether Euclidean geometry was correct by measuring the angles of the triangle formed by three German hilltops (Brocken, Inselsberg, Hohe Hagen). He did not find a deviation of the sum of angles from the Euclidean value of 180 degrees. His successor Riemann took up the idea that geometry is a part of the empirical reality and developed a momentous generalization in which the idea of a curved space was introduced and worked out with mathematical exactness.

In Einstein's theory of gravitation, usually called general relativity, the principle of decidability was used again. He started from the experimentally well-established fact that in a gravitational field the acceleration of all bodies is equal, independent of the mass. An observer in a closed box can therefore not decide whether the acceleration of a body relative to the box is due to a gravitational field or to an acceleration of the box in the opposite direction. From this simple argument the enormous structure of the general theory of relativity was developed. The main mathematical tool was Riemann's geometry mentioned above, applied to the four-dimensional space, which is a combination of ordinary space and time.

I mention all this to illustrate the power and fertility of the principle of decidability. Another success of the principle is quantum mechanics. Bohr's theory of the orbital motion of electrons in the atom had, after a splendid beginning, gotten into difficulties. Heisenberg observed that the theory worked with quantities which were fundamentally unobservable (electronic orbits of definite dimensions and periods) and he sketched a new theory which used only concepts whose validity was empirically decidable. The new mechanics, in the development of which I participated, did away with another of Kant's categories a priori: causality. In classical physics causality was always (doubtlessly also by Kant) interpreted as determinism. The new quantum mechanics was not deterministic but statistical (a point to which I shall return). Its success in all parts of physics is beyond dispute.

I consider it reasonable to apply the principle of decidability also to the philosophical problem of the origin of an objective world picture.

The point from which we started was the skeptical question: how is it possible to infer from the subjective world of experiences the existence of an objective external world? Actually this inference is innate and so natural that to doubt it seems rather absurd. But the doubt exists, and all attempts of a solution, whether of the type of Kant's "thing in itself" or of Lenin's dogma, are unsatisfactory because they violate the principle of decidability.

Now the impossibility to decide—whether the green I see is the same as the green you see—is due to the attempt to agree about one *single* sense impression. No doubt that is impossible.

But for *two* impressions of the same sense organ,

e.g., two colors, there already exist decidable, communicable, objectively testable statements: They refer to the comparison of the two impressions, particularly to equality or inequality. (Instead of equal or unequal it would be better to say indistinguishable or distinguishable; but such psychological refinements do not matter in this logical consideration.) There is no doubt that two individuals can agree about such comparisons. Though I cannot describe to another person what I perceive if I call a thing green, we both can find out and agree whether two leaves which seem to me of the same hue appear to him also of the same hue. Apart from "equality," there exist other pair relations which are communicable and objective; foremost being those of the type more-less, e.g., brighter-darker, stronger-fainter, hotter-colder, harder-softer, and so on. But we need not to discuss these possibilities. The existence of communicable properties of pairs suffices.

In physics this principle of objectivation is known and practiced systematically. Colors, sounds, even shapes are not considered single, but in pairs. Every beginner learns the so-called zero method, for instance, in optics, where an instrument is so set that a perceptual difference of two visual fields (in brightness, hue, saturation) vanishes. The reading of a scale means the observation of a geometrical "equality," the coincidence of the pointer and a line of the scale. A major part of experimental physics consists in this kind of scale reading.

The fact that by comparing pairs communicable, objective statements are possible, has an immense importance because it is the root of speaking and writing, and of the most powerful instrument of thinking, of mathematics. I propose to use for all these means of communication between individuals the term "symbols."

They are easily reproducible, visual or audible signs or signals whose accurate shape is of no importance but for which a crude reproduction suffices. If I write (or pronounce) A and somebody else also writes (or pronounces) A, each of us perceives his own A and that of the other as equal, optically and acoustically. What matters is rough equality or some similarity—the mathematician would say the topological aspect—not particulars such as the pitch of speaking, a flourish and ornament of writing or printing.

Symbols are the carriers of communication between individuals and thus decisive for the possibility of objective knowledge.

In his *Maxims and Reflections,* Goethe says the following: "There is some unknown regularity in the object which corresponds to the unknown regularity in the subject."

I quote this not only because of its relation to our discussion of subjectivity and objectivity but because of the word "correspond." Goethe, with his gift of divination, has used a concept which may be called *Urbegriff* (primary concept) of all learning, knowing, understanding. I say "primary," translating the German syllable *ur*, which Goethe himself uses in many similar instances: "primary plant" (*Urpflanze*) in his doctrine of metamorphoses; "primary phenomenon" (*Urphänomen*) in his theory of colors. Instead of "correspond," one now often uses the word "coordinate," which means making things correspond.

The child learning to speak means that it learns to coordinate words and sentences to things, persons, actions, perceptions. Writing is the coordination of visual symbols to such phenomena or to the corresponding words. Counting is the coordination of the numerals "1, 2, 3, . . ." learned by heart to a sequence of similar things. Modern mathematics has extended this principle to infinite sets of things, in the so-called "theory of sets" (*Mengenlehre*), initiated by Cantor. He has shown, for instance, that one cannot establish such a mutual one-to-one correspondence between the points of a (finite) line and the set of all integers (1, . . . to infinity), which means that infinite sets of different "numbers" exist.

In geometry, points in space are connected with

groups of numbers called "coordinates." Thus to each geometrical fact there corresponds an analytical one, i.e., a theorem in the domain of numbers. The essential feature of mathematics is not numbers but the idea of coordination.* There are extended and fundamental mathematical doctrines, like group theory, where numbers play only an insignificant part. In physics the first not purely mechanical but properly physical discovery is a perfect example of coordination, namely, the discovery by Pythagoras that the natural intervals in music; octave, fifth, fourth, and so on, correspond to the divisions of a vibrating string according to simple ratios $2:1$, $3:2$, $4:3$, and so on. There is actually a double correspondence between perceptions of ear (musical intervals), eye or muscles (length of the string), and numbers.

The measurement of the intensity of heat (temperature) with a thermometer is the coordination of the perception of heat with a geometrical quantity (the length of a mercury column, the position of a gal-

---

* It seems not unnecessary to remark here that the current ideas about the essence of mathematics are somewhat wrong. For instance, it is repeated again and again that the whole of mathematics is a tautology, i.e., self-evident if properly considered. This opinion is expressed by the distinguished biologist and Nobel laureate P. B. Medawar in his book *The Uniqueness of the Individual,* page 15 (London: Methuen & Co., 1957).

vanometer needle) and thus again with a number (scale value).

Chemistry coordinates the substances with combinations of symbols which are abbreviations of the names of a number of elementary substances (atoms). The historical root of this procedure is the fact that by coordinating atomic weights to the symbols of elements one could read off molecular weights from the combination of atomic symbols representing it; and by coordinating valencies to the symbols of atoms one can predict possibilities of reactions. Later this elementary method of describing chemical bonds has been absorbed by the general atomic theory.

In every field of experience this correspondence of sense impressions with symbols has been established. It suffices for the needs of ordinary life: the words and sentences of a language, whether spoken or written, corresponding to perceptions, emotions, and the like, are learned and used without being further analyzed (naïve realism). Thus the mental image of the world is formed by the ordinary human being and refined in literature.

Science goes one step further. I do not know whether what I am going to say holds for all the sciences and the humanities. I wish to speak only about the exact sciences which I know. There mathematical symbols are used, and they have a particularity: they reveal structures.

Mathematics is just the detection and investigation of structures of thinking which lie hidden in the mathematical symbols. The simplest mathematical entity, the chain of integers 1, 2, 3, . . . , consists of symbols which are combined according to certain rules, the arithmetical axioms. The most important of these is an internal coordination: to each integer there is one following it.* These rules determine a vast number of structures; e.g., the prime numbers with their remarkable properties and complicated distribution, the reciprocity theorems of quadratic residues and so on. Geometry has to do with spatial structures which appear analytically as invariants of transformations. Group theory deals with structures which appear when certain sets of operations are repeated, such as the permutations of sets of letters or symmetry operations like rotations or mirror imaging, and others.

These are structures of pure thinking. The transition to reality is made by theoretical physics which

---

* The truth is that mathematics begins only with the establishment and proof of theorems for infinite sets. Thus $1 + 2 + 3 + 4 = 10$ is not a mathematical theorem, but a trivial, verifiable fact. But $1 + 2 + 3 + \cdots + n = \frac{1}{2} n(n + 1)$ for all values $n = 1, 2, . . .$ (without end) is a mathematical theorem, simple to prove but only with the help of a principle beyond ordinary logics (the so-called principle of complete induction).

correlates symbols to observed phenomena. Where this can be done hidden structures are coordinated to phenomena; these very structures are regarded by the physicist as the objective reality lying behind the subjective phenomena.

It is impossible to describe this procedure in its enormous diversity. Only one historical point of view must be stressed: since Newton the structures contained in differential equations have been used and become familiar. The reason is that they permit a direct connection with experiences about ordinary things in daily life. Galileo's mechanics started from such experiences. Then Newton generalized the mechanical concepts in such a way that they could be applied to celestial bodies. The first optical theories used mechanical models. Space was supposed to be filled with a substance called ether which functioned as carrier of vibrations according to the laws of mechanics. Even Maxwell discovered and discussed his field equations at first with the help of concealed mechanisms. In the early days of atomic theory mechanical models were used; in the kinetic theory of gases the atoms were considered to be small elastic balls which recoil from each other and from the walls of the container.

Very slowly and against violent opposition the opinion spread that models were not only unnecessary but even an obstruction to progress.

Symbol and Reality
179

The first important example was Heinrich Hertz's treatment of Maxwell's theory of the electromagnetic field. Hertz cannot be called an exclusive theoretician, for to him we owe the experimental verification of the theory through his discovery of electromagnetic waves. But he regarded the electromagnetic field as an entity in its own right which ought to be described without mechanical models.

Since then the development has irresistibly proceeded in this direction. A natural phenomenon need not be reduced to models accessible to imagination and explicable in mechanical terms, but has its own mathematical structure directly derived from experience.

This change of outlook was decisive when Planck, in 1900, discovered in an investigation of heat radiation a new constant of nature, the quantum of action. This did not fit at all into the system of Newtonian mechanics and the physical theories built on its pattern. It is true, the models of electronic motions in atoms suggested by Niels Bohr were a micro-imitation of planetary motion. However, not all orbits were "allowed" but only certain "stationary" states characterized by unmechanical "quantum conditions," and the transitions between these states, the "quantum jumps," followed rules which have no analogy in mechanics. When this development culminated in the establishment of quantum mechanics there was an end to mechanical models and, by the way, also to the causal description of classical physics.

Thus physical research has won a freedom necessary to handle the ever increasing amount of observations and measurements. We try to find the mathematics appropriate to a domain of experience; then we investigate its structure and regard it as representing physical reality, whether it conforms to accustomed things or not. As examples I mention the curved space of the macro-world (cosmology) and the atoms, nuclei, elementary particles in the micro-world; they have little in common with our familiar surroundings.

Yet a further freedom had to be gained before physics could claim the right to call the structures images of the reality behind the phenomena.

Philosophy has always, and still is, inclined to make final, categorical statements. Science was strongly influenced by this tendency. The early physicists, for example, considered the determinism of Newtonian mechanics of particular merit.

But already in the eighteenth century the concept of probability appears in physics. In attempts to establish a molecular theory of gases observable quantities, such as pressure, were conceived as averages of molecular collisions. In the nineteenth century the kinetic theory of gases was fully developed, followed by statistical mechanics applicable to all substances, gaseous, liquid, and solid. The concept of probability was applied systematically and built into the system of physics.

This procedure was usually justified by the human inability to handle enormous numbers of particles with rigorous methods; but the elementary process, e.g., the collisions of two atoms, was assumed to obey the laws of classical, deterministic physics.*

After the discovery of quantum mechanics this assumption became obsolete. The elementary processes are not obeying deterministic, but statistical laws according to the statistical interpretation of quantum mechanics.

I am convinced that ideas such as absolute certainty, absolute precision, final truth, and so on are phantoms which should be excluded from science.

From the restricted knowledge of the present state of a system one can, with the help of a theory, deduce conjectures and expectations of a future situation, expressed in terms of probability. Each statement of

* The deterministic interpretation of Newtonian mechanics is actually an unjustified idealization, as Brillouin and I have independently shown. It is based on the idea of absolutely precise measurements, an assumption which has obviously no physical meaning. It is not difficult to write classical mechanics in a statistical form.

probability is, from the standpoint of the theory used, either right or wrong.*

This relaxation of the rules of thinking seems to me the greatest blessing which modern science has given us. For the belief that there is only one truth and that oneself is in possession of it, seems to me the deepest root of all that is evil in the world.

Before doing the last step in these considerations, I wish to recall the point of departure, namely, the shock experienced by every thoughtful person when comprehending that a single sense impression is not communicable, hence purely subjective. Anybody who has not had this experience will regard the whole discussion as sophistry. In a certain sense this is right. For naïve realism is a natural attitude which corresponds to the biological situation of the human race, just as in that of the animal world. A bee recognizes flowers by their color or scent and needs no philosophy. As long as one restricts himself to the things of everyday life the problem of objectivity is an artifact of philosophical brooding.

* Here I apply the logical rule of the "excluded third" (*tertium non datur*). The question has been investigated, in particular in connection with quantum theory, whether a "three-valued logic" can be established where between "right" and "wrong" there is a third possibility "indeterminate." But I cannot discuss this here.

In science, however, it is different. Here one often has to do with phenomena beyond everyday experience. What you see through a high-power microscope, what you perceive with the help of a telescope, spectroscope, or one of the various amplifying devices of electronics is incomprehensible without a theory; it must be interpreted. In the smallest domain as in the largest, in that of atoms as well as of stars, we encounter phenomena which do not resemble the accustomed aspect of our surroundings and can be described only with the help of abstract concepts. Here the question cannot be eluded whether there is an objective world, independent of the observer, behind the phenomena.

I do not believe that this question can be answered categorically by logical thinking. But it can if we make use of the freedom to consider an extremely improbable statement as wrong.

The assumption that the coincidence of structures revealed by using different sense organs and communicable from one individual to the other is accidental, is improbable to the highest degree.

This is the normal way of scientific reasoning, and apart from science of all research. For example, an archaeologist who discovers in two different countries remains of pottery similar in design will conclude that this cannot be accidental but indicates a common origin.

I am not afraid of identifying such well-defined structures with Kant's "thing in itself." The objections quoted before in the formulation of Bertrand Russell have no validity from our point of view. They consist in the following: The existence of the "thing in itself" is postulated because one needs an external cause to understand why different individuals experience "the same" phenomena; but the category of causality has a meaning only within the domain of phenomena. However, the concept of causality is a residue of former ways of thinking and is replaced today by the process of coordination as described before. This procedure leads to structures which are communicable, controllable, hence objective. It is justified to call these by the old term "thing in itself." They are pure form, void of all sensual qualities. That is all we can wish and expect.

This result of course contradicts the traditional conception of Kant's "thing in itself." Hegel, for example, says in the *Encyclopedia of Philosophy*, section 44: "The thing in itself . . . means the object as far as everything referring to consciousness, feeling, emotion as well as to all notions is abstracted. It is easy to see what is left—the perfect abstractum, the complete emptiness, just something from a 'world beyond' (*Jenseits*). . . ."

If the objects of modern physics, in particular those of atomic physics, are identified with Kant's "thing in itself," one can agree with Hegel that they are a "perfect abstractum." But that they are perfectly empty, something from a world beyond, does not fit the facts. Remember what practical use can be made of them in the production of things like engines, airplanes, nuclear reactors, plastics, electronic computers, ad infinitum. It might happen that nuclear research leads to our being transferred to the "world beyond." Yet Hegel did not mean this and could not foresee it.

The systems of formulae in physics do not necessarily represent conceivable things, familiar through experience. Yet they are derived from experience through abstraction and continually checked by experiment. On the other hand, the instruments used by the physicists are made of materials known in ordinary life and can be described in everyday language. The results obtained with the help of these instruments, such as exposed photographic plates, tables of figures or curves, are also of this kind. The trace of droplets in a Wilson expansion chamber suggests a particle in flight; a periodical distribution of the blackening on a photographic plate suggests interferences of waves. One cannot give up such interpretations without paralyzing intuition, which is the source of research, and rendering communication between scientists more difficult.

Therefore physicists are bound to describe the content of their abstract formulae as far as possible in terms of ordinary language with concepts based on intuition. The specific difficulties encountered here have been studied by the Copenhagen school under the leadership of Niels Bohr. He has shown that it is possible to describe atomic processes with the "classical" concepts, provided one desists from investigating *all* properties of a physical system simultaneously. Different, mutually exclusive but complementary experimental arrangements are needed. The experimentalist has the choice which of them to employ. Thus a subjective trend is reintroduced into physics and cannot be eliminated. Another loss of objectivity is due to the fact that the theory makes only probability predictions, which produce graded expectations. From our standpoint where subjectivity is primary and the possibility of objective knowledge problematic it is not surprising that the rigorous separation of subject and object is not possible if one tries to express the mathematical formalism with the help of images.

Bohr's principle of complementarity is another new method of thinking. Discovered in physics, it is applicable to many other fields. It is another loosening of traditional methods of thought which promises important results. But this leads beyond the frame of these considerations.

I wish to mention that the latest branch of physical research, the theory of elementary particles, seems to be still entirely in the abstract. Though it leads to definite observable predictions the elementary processes themselves can hardly be grasped by intuition. The content of Heisenberg's world formula seems to me at present an abstract "thing in itself" without an immediate correlation with sense impressions.

Here it may be remarked that a turning toward the abstract appears to be an obvious trend of our time. We observe it also in art, particularly in abstract painting and sculpture. But this parallelism is only seeming. For modern painters seem to me to avoid associations and intellectual interpretations, and concentrate on appealing to the optical sensation. The physicist, on the other hand, uses the perceptions of the senses as material to construct an intellectual world. The word "abstract" refers in both cases to opposite intentions.

Yet we scientists should always remember that all experience is based on the senses. A theoretician who, immersed in his formulae, forgets the phenomena which he wants to explain is no real scientist, physicist, or chemist; and if he is estranged by his books from the beauty and variety of nature, I would call him a poor fool. At present we have a reasonable equilibrium between experiment and theory, between sensual and intellectual reality, and we ought to see that it is preserved.

We also have to be careful that scientific thinking in abstract terms does not extend to other domains where it is not applicable. Human and ethical values cannot be based on scientific thinking. It is true that Kant has attempted to build up an ethical system according to the model of categories, by introducing his "categorical imperative." But the validity of this command is not "decidable" in the sense of the word as defined by us. It simply has to be accepted and believed in. However attractive and satisfactory abstract thinking is for the scientist, however valuable his results for the material aspect of our civilization, it is most dangerous to apply these methods beyond the range of their validity, to religion, ethics, art, literature, and all humanities.

Thus my excursion into philosophy is intended to be not only an illustration of the foundation of science, but also an exhortation to restrict the scientific methods to that domain where they reasonably belong.

SIX

What Is Left to Hope For?

Hope is a word one is unlikely to find in the literature of physics. A paper starts with the planning of an experiment or with a theory based on an expectation. But there is hardly any mention of hope.

However, when I recall my actual experiences during a long scientific career, I have one ineradicable memory: the disappointment when a result was different from what I had expected. But disappointment could only occur when there was hope.

No science is absolutely separate from life. Even the most dispassionate scientist is at the same time a human being; he would like to be right, to see his intuition confirmed; he would like to make a name for himself, to be a success. Such hopes are motives for his work, just as is the thirst for knowledge.

Today, the belief in the possibility of a clear separation between objective knowledge and the pursuit of knowledge has been destroyed by science itself. In the operation of science and in its ethics a change has taken place that makes it impossible to maintain the old ideal of the pursuit of knowledge for its own sake which my generation believed in. We were convinced that this could never lead to any evil since the search for truth was good in itself. That was a beautiful dream from which we were awakened by world events. Even the deepest sleepers awoke when, in August 1945, the first atom bombs fell on Japanese cities.

Since then, we have realized that through the results of our own work we are completely entangled with human life, its economy and politics, with the social struggle for power among the states, and that we therefore bear a great responsibility.

In my opinion, the atom bomb was only the last link of a development that can be traced far back and that is now leading toward a crisis, possibly toward a final, devastating catastrophe. Any hope of preventing this can only be based on an understanding of the course that led us into the present situation.

It is neither given to me nor is it my business to speak about hope in an abstract philosophical way. I can only tell about my own experiences and to what expectations they led me. I would like to show by way of certain examples how technical science applied to war has led to the gradual demolition of ethical restraints up to the present situation where there are no more restraints left. From this position there is no advance in the same direction. It is only possible to halt and then, perhaps, to turn back. That is what we may hope for.

My first knowledge of the role of modern technology in war came from history lessons at school: for instance, how the needle gun helped the Prussian army to win the war against Austria in 1866, yet how the French lost the war of 1870-1871 despite their possession of the superior bolt-action rifle, the *chassepot*. This shows that, at that time, technical superiority seems to have been very important but not decisive. However, the inherent ethical danger was recognized and was met with the idea of humanization of war which found its expression in the Red Cross and in the Geneva Conventions concerning forbidden weapons, protection of the civilian population, and so on.

In World War I, things developed in a different way. The war began in the old fashion with marches and battles. But soon the character of the battles changed basically. The combat zones became stationary and trench warfare developed, combined with repeated attempts to break out of it through concentration of artillery. The soldier became more and more a mere target, an object of destruction by superhuman forces supplied by technical science. The decisive factor was the power of the industrial capacity and technical inventiveness of the hinterland.

I myself played a tiny part in this machine as a member of a military authority in Berlin, where I worked together with other physicists on the so-called sound-ranging method. This method determined the emplacement of an enemy gun by measuring the moment of arrival of the report from firing at various observation posts. Even in this small, not very important field it was evident that everything depended on the industrial situation as a whole. The instruments for precise time measurement which we demanded from the authorities to make the method more effective were refused because the industry would not spare the time, labor, and materials for such trifles. The British, however, did not economize when it came to such demands.

The view the war offered the observer who was not confused by patriotic propaganda was this: the male youth were sacrificed in a battle that was actually decided by the hinterland's technology and supply of raw materials. Even then, this seemed most immoral and inhuman to me, and I began to understand that henceforth not heroism but technology had become decisive in war, and that in human society technology has made war obsolete.

What Is Left to Hope For?

Let me mention two experiences from World War I to illustrate this, both of them connected with the name of the great chemist Fritz Haber. Shortly before the war broke out, he had invented a method to fix atmospheric nitrogen (as nitric acid) and had thereby created the first artificial fertilizer, saltpeter. Now this, as is well known, is also a component of gunpowder. The German general staff had seemingly provided for everything but had not considered that saltpeter came from Chile and this import was now cut off by the blockade. Without Haber's invention, the war might possibly have been lost for Germany after six months because of lack of gunpowder. Thus, the scientific idea and the technical capability to put it to use were in this case decisive factors of world history.

The second time Haber intervened in order to break out of the stationary trench warfare and get the front moving: he invented chemical warfare—the use of poison gas (starting with chlorine, then other much more harmful gases) in order to drive the enemy out of the trenches. This method was at first successful. But its dependence upon wind and weather and the invention of the gas mask limited its effectiveness and, further, the enemy soon knew how to use it to the same or even greater extent.

Many of my colleagues took part in this work, even men of strong ethical convictions. As to Haber, so to them the defense of the fatherland was the supreme commandment. As for myself, I felt a conflict of conscience. The issue was not whether gas grenades were more inhuman than high-explosive shells but whether poison, whch had been considered an instrument of cowardly murder from time immemorial, should be sanctioned as a war weapon, for without a limitation of the allowable soon everything might be allowed. But only years later, in fact after Hiroshima, did clear convictions begin to take shape in me. Otherwise, an awareness of the scientist's social responsibility would certainly have found expression in my earlier educational work and perhaps not so many of my pupils would have been ready to collaborate on the atom bomb.

That I was not alone with my doubts even during World War I was revealed to me by an experience in 1933 when I came to Cambridge in England as a refugee. I was received with great kindness, while Haber, who had been forced to emigrate despite his services to the German cause in World War I, was not welcome. Lord Rutherford, the founder of nuclear physics and one of the greatest physicists of our time, declined an invitation to my house because Haber was to be present also; he did not want to shake hands with the inventor of chemical warfare. Rutherford had played a great part in the technical defense of his country and was by no means a pacifist. But he drew a line beyond which an instrument of extermination was not to be considered a weapon. I believe he would have explained that, without a moral demarcation for the use of weapons, there could be no limit to devastation and that this could bring about the end of civilization.

This opinion has been justified. Chemical warfare was a decisive moral defeat of humanity. Although poison gas was not used in World War II and although Geneva Conventions have prohibited it, organizations for the study and prosecution of chemical warfare have been created by all military powers. A state would hardly shrink from putting one of these to use if it should prove of military advantage.

After the moral restraints concerning chemical warfare were thrown overboard, there followed the collapse of the principle which had been accepted in the nineteenth century—that states may conduct a war only against the military forces of their enemies but not against their civilian populations.

I am not a specialist in international law and have read but little of Grotius and his successors. Thus I cannot present a history of this principle but only my impressions from events I witnessed. It is clear that the civilian population has always suffered severely from wars if they lived in the combat zone. The starvation of besieged cities and of entire countries (even with the cessation of hostilities, as after World War I) also seems to have been considered "allowable."

This barrier broke down during World War II as a result of the development of the air force. Germany was in the lead with air raids on open cities—Warsaw and other Polish cities, then Rotterdam, Oslo, Coventry, the systematic bombardment of London after Dunkirk. I was in Edinburgh at that time and often heard scornful remarks from colleagues and friends about this immoral type of warfare whose pattern England would never follow. But this prediction proved false.

How did it happen? The leading lights in the decision on bombing warfare were two British scientists, Tizard and Lindemann. The beginning of their careers was similar: after a brilliant start in research, doubts may have risen in both men whether they would belong among the peers of science. Thus, they turned to administration and politics.

Tizard became chairman of the committee for air defense and earned great acclaim for his role in developing the radar method for air warfare at the right time, enabling the small British air force to win the famous "battle of Britain," thus thwarting the plan of a German invasion.

Lindemann's influence too was based on his work in technical warfare but even more on his friendship with Winston Churchill. This went back to an incident in World War I, when Lindemann proved the accuracy of a calculation on stabilization of certain airplanes by piloting one of them himself and pulling it out of a spin. After this demonstration of ingenuity and courage, Churchill had absolute confidence in Lindemann, made him his first scientific adviser, and conferred a peership on him under the name of Lord Cherwell.

In 1942, Lindemann-Cherwell suggested using the British bomber squadrons to destroy the workers' residential areas in large German cities. Tizard, however, believed that an air attack against military targets would be much more effective; whether the inhumanity of the first plan mattered to him, I do not know. Churchill sided with his friend Cherwell. Later, it became evident that Cherwell's estimation of the damage that would be done by the thousand bomber raids was approximately six times too high, that these air raids were not decisive for the outcome of the war, and that Tizard had been right.

So it happened that the German cities fell, burying hundreds of thousands of civilians under their ruins. With them fell once more a moral barrier against barbarism. Evil was met with greater evil and this again with even greater: I mean the so-called super-weapons that were later used by the Germans. These were the first examples of the inhuman method of killing by remote control, without personal risk and thus without personal responsibility: that is, purely technical warfare, "pushbutton war."

An expert on international law might illustrate this outline of the tragic history of moral decline through many more examples: for example, from war at sea since the introduction of submarines—remember the sinking of the *Lusitania* in World War I.

Under the influence of technology, the parties at war have gone so far as to exterminate deliberately the civilian population and justify this as right. Let us take a look at the numerical proportions of civilians and soldiers killed in the last three big wars that were still conducted without atomic weapons.

In World War I, the total number of killed was approximately ten million, 95 per cent of whom were soldiers and 5 per cent civilians. In World War II, more than fifty million were killed, comprising almost equal numbers of soldiers and civilians (52 per cent to 48 per cent). During the war in Korea, of the nine million dead, 84 per cent were civilians and only 16 per cent soldiers. Whoever still believes in war as a legitimate instrument of politics and clings to the traditional ideas of a hero's death for sake of wife and child and defense of the homeland should now realize that these are fairy tales and not pleasant ones at that.

Nuclear weapons have driven this development

to extremes, as everyone knows. One cannot blame the men who at that time (1939–1945) worked on nuclear fission, because the discovery of uranium fission came from Hitler Germany and one had to assume that the Nazis would do anything to develop it into a weapon against which there was no resistance. This had to be prevented.

But when in the United States the first bomb was ready for use, Hitler Germany had already surrendered and Japan was also at her last gasp, having already, through diplomatic channels, even asked for peace.

Then, everything happened as in the Cherwell-Tizard dispute. The military leaders, especially General Groves, who had headed the nuclear energy project, thought only of the immediate military advantages and calculated how many lives would be saved if Japan were forced to surrender without an invasion. Japanese lives, of course, were not considered. Groves, moreover, did not want to sacrifice the satisfaction of demonstrating "his" achievement in all its horror to the world. He did not even let the scientists who had actually made the achievement have any say in the matter. Among the latter was a group of reasonable men who accurately predicted the long-term consequence of dropping this bomb on Japanese cities and, in the so-called

Franck Report, warned the government accordingly. The contrary decision, however, was made by a committee appointed by President Truman to advise him, and whose members included several outstanding physicists. These members followed Cherwell's example and thus the borderline was finally crossed that leads onto the downhill road to possible self-annihilation of the human race.

I have only to indicate briefly what transpired: attempts to put nuclear technology on an international basis failed. Russia caught up to America a lot sooner than was expected. The invention of the hydrogen bomb in America was very soon followed by the Soviet Union's invention. Then followed the development of intercontinental ballistic missiles in competition between the two great powers, with the exploration of space program serving as a cover-up. Each of the great powers now has enough nuclear weapons to annihilate the human race many times over.

The politicians know what is at stake and they maneuver so as to maintain the balance of terror. But the balance is unstable. The people become indifferent to the danger because of the spreading moral paralysis; the politicians become more cynical and risk advances again and again that can tip the balance—as in the Cuban crisis.

What is there left to hope for? Can one hope that the insight of mankind into the atomic danger will bring salvation?

The only thing that can save us is an old dream of the human race: world peace and world organization. These were regarded as unattainable, as utopian. It was believed that human nature is unchangeable, and since there had always been war there would always be war.

Today this is no longer acceptable. Universal peace in a world that has become smaller is no longer utopian but a necessity, a condition for the survival of the human race. The opinion that this is so spreads farther and farther. The immediate result is a paralysis of politics, because a convincing method of achieving political goals without a threat of force, with war as a last resort, has not yet been discovered.

Many wise people think about this problem and I am convinced that a solution could be found if there were plenty of time at our disposal. This expectation is based on the experiences of a long life. Innumerable are the things that now exist that in my youth were considered utopian. My fields of science, atomistics and electronics, which have led to a deep understanding of the structure of matter, were then at their very beginnings. Anyone who would have described the techrical applications of this knowledge as we have them today would have been laughed at. There were no automobiles, no airplanes, no wireless communication, no radio, no movies, no television, no assembly line, no mass production, and so on. All these have come into existence since my youth and have created economic and social changes in the lives of the people that are deeper and more fundamental than anything in the previous ten thousand years of history: semifeudal empires have become socialist republics; scattered Negro tribes have become organized states with modern constitutions; space research has begun and nobody gets excited about the most daring, most expensive plans of the astronauts.

But for the one question, the most important by far: can political, economical, ideological disputes be decided only by means of force and war? The postulate of the unchangeability of human nature is to remain unchallenged: since it has always been like this, it will always be like this.

To me, this seems absurd even when it is preached by great politicians and philosophers. Unless this axiom is rejected, the human race is condemned to destruction. Our hope is based on the union of two spiritual powers: the moral awareness of the unacceptability of a war degenerated to mass murder of the defenseless and the rational knowledge of the incompatibility of technological warfare with the survival of the human race.

The only question is whether we have enough time to let these realizations become effective. For the present situation is highly unstable and through its own mechanisms becomes increasingly dangerous day by day. The miscalculation of an individual or an apparatus, the blind passion of a leader, the ideological or national delusion of the masses can at any moment lead to a catastrophe. We may not be spared a terrifying event before a change in thinking and action occurs.

But we must hope. There are two kinds of hope. If one hopes for good weather or for winning a pool, then hope has no influence whatsoever on what happens, and if it rains or if we draw a blank we have to resign ourselves to actuality. But in the coexistence of people, especially in politics, hope is a moving force. Only if we hope do we act in order to bring fulfillment of the hope nearer. We must not tire of fighting the immorality and unreasonableness which today still govern the world.

I would like to quote here the words of a great man, not a politician or philosopher but a man of practical reasoning, the physician and Nobel Prize winner Gerhard Domagk, whose chemotherapeutic discoveries have preserved the health and life of countless individuals. It is as he says, "a confession, a beseeching that is at the same time a warning and yet full of hope," and it is expressed as follows:

"What is really important in this world? That we individuals get along with each other, try to understand and help each other as best we can. For us physicians that is natural. Why shouldn't it also be possible for all other people? Don't tell me this [would] be Utopia! Every discovery was considered utopian. Why should we first wait for another measuring of powers—we really did suffer enough to have become wise. But it is comfortable to cling to old customs; more comfortable to follow violent rulers, cholerics, paranoiacs, and other mentally disturbed individuals rather than thinking for oneself and looking for new ways of reconciliation instead of mutual destruction."

These are plain words. They come from a man who fights for life, from a man who does not merely hope to save human beings from sickness but puts all his knowledge and ability to work for it.

It depends on us, on each individual citizen in every country of the world, for a stop to be put to the existing nonsense. Today, it is no longer the cholera or plague bacillus that threatens us but the traditional, cynical reasoning of politicians, the indifference of the masses, and the physicists' and other scientists' evasion of responsibility. That which they have done, as I tried to explain, cannot be undone: knowledge cannot be extinguished, and technology has its own laws. But scientists could and should use the respect that they gain through their knowledge and ability to show the politicians the way back to reasonableness and humanity, as the Göttingen Eighteen once tried.

All of us must fight against official lies and encroachments; against the assertions that there is protection from nuclear weapons through shelters and emergency regulations; against the suppression of those who enlighten the public about it; against narrow-minded nationalism, *gloire,* greed for dominance, and we must especially fight against those ideologies which pronounce the infallibility of their doctrines and thus separate the world into irreconcilable camps.

There is still hope, but it will only achieve fulfillment if we stake everything on the battle against the diseases of our time.

Appendix

The following distinguished scientists worked with me at the Institutes of Theoretical Physics in Frankfurt and Göttingen during the time of my directorship (1919-1921 and 1921-1932).

ASSOCIATES: W. Heisenberg (Nobel laureate), W. Heitler, E. Hückel, F. Hund, L. Nordheim, W. Pauli (Nobel laureate), L. Rosenfeld, and O. Stern (Nobel laureate).

DOCTOR'S DEGREE: M. Delbrück, W. Elsasser, Marie Goeppert-Mayer (Nobel laureate), F. Hund, P. Jordan, and J. R. Oppenheimer.

COLLABORATORS: V. Fock, E. Hylleraas, A. Lane, J. Mayer, G. Rumer, Y. Sugiura, and N. Wiener.

VISITORS (participants in the regular colloquium or in my private evening discussions; some took part in the research that went on in the department):

E. U. Condon, P. Dirac (Nobel laureate), E. Fermi (Nobel laureate), J. I. Frenkel, O. Klein, J. E. Lennard-Jones, F. London, N. Mott, J. von Neumann, L. Pauling (Nobel laureate), J. E. Tamm (Nobel laureate), E. Teller, and E. P. Wigner (Nobel laureate).

Index

Index

Institute of Theoretical Physics, Frankfurt, 207
Institute of Theoretical Physics, Göttingen, 207
intercontinental ballistic missiles, 157, 201
isotopes, 124
Italy, 38

Japan, 83, 191
Japanese cities, 200-201
"Jewish physics," 72, 98
Joffe, A., 145
Jordan, P., 34, 207

Kant, Immanuel, 162-165, 170, 172, 185, 186, 189
Kapitza, Peter, 40
Karman, Theodor von, 25, 26, 27
Kemp-Smith, 42
Klein, Felix, 18, 20-21
Klein, O., 208
Knipping, 26
Koenigsberg, 18
Korean War, 199-200
Kun Huang, 41

Ladenburg, Rudolf, 18
Landé, A., 29, 31, 207
Larmor, Joseph, 24
lattice dynamics, 27
lattice energies, 31
lattice vibrations, 26
Laue, Max von, 26, 30
laws of mechanics, 92

Lenin, 167, 172
Lertes, P., 32
Leukippos, 71, 97
Lindau, Lake Constance, 80, 85
Lindemann, F., 197
Lennard-Jones, J. E., 208
Lobatschefski, N. I., 170
Locke, John, 163
London, F., 208
London, England, 197
Lorenz, R., 31
Ludwig, W., 45
Lummer, O., 24
Lusitania, 199

Mach, Ernst, 166
Madelung, G., 29
Magdalen College, Oxford, 6, 42
magneto-hydrodynamics, 32
Mainau Statement, 80, 85, 113
Marconi, Guglielmo, 16
Margenau, Henry, 54, 166
Marx, Karl, 167
Marxism, 148
Maschke, Erich, 16
mass murder, 203-204
Massachusetts Institute of Technology, 36
mathematical symbols, 178-179
matrix mechanics, 34
Maxwell, J. C., 30
Maxwell's theory, 39, 168, 179-180